CUTTING E

ADVANCED

WORKBOOK

peter moor   sarah cunningham

Contents

Module 6

Module 7

Module 8

Module 9

Module 10

module 1

Vocabulary

What does globalisation mean for us?

1 **a)** Write the correct word or phrase next to the definition.

~~brand~~ multi-ethnic goods domestic clash mass non-native speaker ~~chain~~ way of life worldwide corporation network standard of living immigration

1 ....*brand*............ (*noun*) a type of product made by a particular company
2 .... (*noun phrase*) how you live in terms of money, accommodation, consumer products, etc.
3 .... (*noun phrase*) people's customs, habits, etc.
4 .... (*noun*) a set of shops / hotels / restaurants which are all similar and are owned by the same organisation
5 .... (*noun*) a group of companies forming a single, large organisation
6 .... (*noun*) an argument or fight between two or more groups of people with different ideas / values
7 .... (*adjective*) happening / produced in a single country
8 .... (*noun*) things that are produced in order to be sold
9 .... (*noun*) a system of wires, roads or electronic connections that intersect and are connected to each other
10 .... (*adjective*) involving a very large number of people
11 .... (*noun phrase*) someone who has learned a particular language as a foreign language, rather than as their native tongue
12 .... (*noun*) the process of entering another country in order to live there
13 .... (*adjective*) having a variety of different races and nationalities
14 .... (*adjective*) appearing or occurring everywhere in the world

b) Write one of the words or phrases in the gap to make a common phrase.

1 fast-food *chain*..........
2 a best-selling drinks ....
3 a simpler ....
4 .... society
5 .... of cultures
6 a rail ....
7 electrical ....
8 a multinational ....
9 .... policy
10 a .... of English
11 gross .... product (= GDP)
12 high ....
13 .... emigration
14 .... phenomenon

2 **a)** Match the words in column A to a word or phrase from column B which has the same meaning.

A	B
1 majestic	a difficult to find
2 flock	b holding tightly
3 elusive	c extremely beautiful
4 lure	d very attractive and tempting
5 enticing	e easy to find
6 clutching	f have no respect for something
7 euphoric	g big and impressive
8 disdain	h attraction
9 plush	i surrounding area
10 commonplace	j luxurious
11 environs	k very happy and excited
12 stunning	l go somewhere in large numbers

b) Choose five of the words from Column A. Write a sentence showing the meaning of each word

The temple is one of the most majestic sights in the city...........
....
....
....
....
....
....
....

Word building

3 Complete the sentences below by changing the word in capitals to the correct form (noun, adjective, etc.). If necessary, use a good monolingual dictionary (e.g. *The Longman Dictionary of Contemporary English*) to help you.

Before you write your answer, check the following points.

- Think about what kind of word is required (noun, adjective, etc.), e.g. *tradition* (noun) → *traditional* (adjective).
- In many cases, there may be more than one noun / adjective, etc. Check the dictionary definition to make sure you get the right one (e.g. *immigrant* / *immigration*).
- Think about whether you need to add a prefix (e.g. *un-*, *over-*, *under-*).

Pronunciation

Three varieties of English

4 [1.1] Listen to the words/ phrases below pronounced first with a 'standard English' accent, then with American and Australian accents. What differences do you hear? Practise saying the one you prefer.

a way of life
b floor
c international crime
d neither here nor there
e fast food
f society
g brand
h ethnic diversity
i in the past
j capital city
k mass tourism
l apart from that

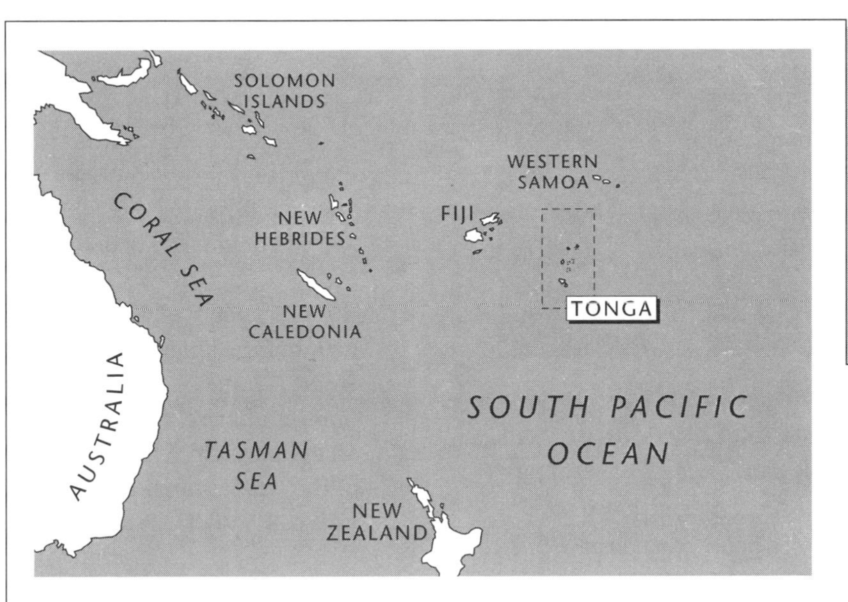

Tonga

1 *Pule'anga Fakatu'i'o Tonga* – also known as the Kingdom of Tonga – is an archipelago of 170 islands in the South Pacific northeast of New Zealand. Uniquely, it has never been colonised by a foreign power and still retains a (1) ..*traditional*.. monarchy. **TRADITION**

5 The economy is based on agriculture, but with industry virtually non-existent, (2) .... goods are crucial to the nation's economy. **IMPORT**

Of Tonga's 97,000 inhabitants, 98% are of Tongan origin; there is relatively little ethnic (3) .... , although in recent years there **DIVERSE**

has been some (4) .... from neighbouring Fiji. Thanks to **IMMIGRATE**

10 foreign (5) .... – mainly from Japan – there is now an **INVEST**

(6) .... airport, at Tongatapu, which has direct flights from Australia, New Zealand and the USA. **NATION**

Modern health care is now available (7) .... , although patients have to be flown to Australia or New Zealand for more **LOCAL**

15 sophisticated surgery.

Tongans are keen to retain their (8) .... identity, so there has **CULTURE**

been some resistance to encouraging mass (9) .... as there are **TOURIST**

fears this might lead to the (10) .... of Tongan life and a **AMERICA**

consequent loss of national identity.

Grammar: continuous verb forms

General

5 Underline the most suitable form of the verb in the text below.

J12 Meeting Opens Tomorrow in Kanalgirie

1 Over the last few hours, hundreds of delegates from all over the world (1) *are arriving / arrived / have been arriving* for the J12
5 meeting of leading industrialised nations, which this year (2) *had been taking place / is taking place / took place* in the quiet Canadian mountain resort of Kanalgirie. The
10 Canadian President, Bernard Leroy, (3) *has been delivering / has delivered / will be delivering* the opening address when the Conference opens tomorrow
15 morning. The Canadian police, who (4) *are preparing / have been preparing / prepared* for the event since late last year, (5) *are taking / take / took* huge precautions to
20 avoid the violence which (6) *has been marking / marked / was marking* last year's summit in Berlin. They (7) *have thrown / have been throwing / throw* an
25 18km security cordon around the area, and last night they (8) *are not allowing / have not been allowing / were not allowing* anyone to pass through –
30 including journalists who usually (9) *are having / have / were having* full access to the delegates. From tomorrow, police (10) *have also been blocking / were also*
35 *blocking / will also be blocking* all mobile phone signals – to prevent bombs being triggered by remote control, a police spokesman (11) *has said / said / was saying*
40 last night.
'The politicians here seem (12) *to be isolating / to isolate / to have been isolating* themselves from the free press,' said one journalist.
45 'There's no doubt that governments (13) *are becoming / become / were becoming* more and more security conscious and less and less concerned with personal
50 freedom. (14) *It gets / It's getting / It will be getting* harder and harder for us to gain access to the people who, over the next few days, (15) *are making / have been*
55 *making / will be making* decisions which will affect all our lives … and that's something that should concern us all.'

Special uses of continuous forms

6 Complete the sentences with the correct form of the verb in brackets.

a 'Have you got any plans for the summer?'
'Yes, ...we're spending...... (we / spend) a couple of weeks at my uncle's house in the mountains.'

b Shall we ring your parents to say why we're late? They must .... (get) worried.

c How can we decide on where to spend our holiday if .... (you / constantly / change) your mind?

d Are you going home already? .... (I / hope) you'd give me a hand with the washing-up.

e Stuart .... (forever / devise) ridiculous schemes which he thinks will attract more business.

f Let's call Patrick. He might .... (know) the answer.

g This isn't really a good time to phone him. He might .... (work) on his assignment.

h I find it very annoying that you .... (always / compare) my cooking to your mother's.

i 'Excuse me … my friend and I .... (wonder) if you'd mind having your photograph taken with us.'

j You really must .... (make) more of an effort to make friends.

Verbs which change meaning in continuous and simple forms

7 Choose the best form of the verb in brackets to complete the sentences.

a I ....*expect*........... (expect / have expected / am expecting / was expecting) you're wondering why I asked you all here today. Well, let me explain …

b 'Is something the matter? You look worried.'
'No, I .... (think / thought / have thought / 'm thinking) about how to tell my parents the bad news, that's all.'

c From the shopkeeper's puzzled expression, I could see that James .... (has / had / was having / is having) a lot of difficulty making himself understood.

d We .... (admire / have admired / are admiring / were admiring) the painting on the staircase as we came up. Is it a portrait of your grandfather?

e Look at that! I haven't worn these jeans for nearly eight years and they .... (still fit / still fitted / are still fitting / were still fitting) perfectly!

f There .... (appeared / appears / is appearing / was appearing) to have been a mistake in processing your order, Mr Phillips. We do apologise.

g I .... (see / saw / 'm seeing / was seeing) the chief executive this afternoon – is there anything you want me to say to her?

h Of all the players you have played against, who is the one you .... (admire / are admiring / were admiring / have been admiring) the most?

i As you can see, I .... (weigh / have been weighing / 'm weighing / was weighing) the flour on my kitchen scales as it's very important to have exactly the right quantity … there we are, 100g exactly.

j I'm sorry, but I .... (don't see / didn't see / am not seeing / wasn't seeing) how we can get all this work done by next Tuesday.

k An adult goliath beetle .... (is weighing / weighs / was weighing / weighed) 70–100g – the same as an apple!

l I don't know why everyone .... (is / was / is being / was being) so irritable today. They're not normally like this.

m When .... (are you thinking / do you think / have you been thinking / were you thinking) you'll be able to get the work finished?

n The good news is that Pamela .... (expects / has expected / is expecting / will be expecting) a baby early next year.

Patterns to notice

Introducing points in an argument

8 **a)** Read the text below about global tourism.

Global Tourism

Tourism is the world's biggest industry. In 1995 there were 567 million tourists worldwide; this number is expected to rise to 937 million by 2010. With improved transport, cheaper flights and increased leisure time, many of the countries of the developing world are rapidly becoming tourist meccas. Since the 1960s, mass tourism has become increasingly specialised, encompassing sporting and adventure holidays as well as ecological tours. Although the tourist industry employs 127 million people worldwide, the benefits of tourism are not always felt at a local level, where jobs are often low paid and menial. Unregulated growth of tourism is causing both environmental and social damage.

b) Using the information in the text and / or your own ideas, complete the sentences below.

1 The main consideration is *whether the growth of tourism actually helps people.*
2 One point to consider about the tourism industry is ....
3 The most important disadvantage of increasing tourism is ....
4 Another disadvantage is ....
5 A further drawback is ....
6 The main problem is ....
7 A further concern is ....
8 One explanation for the growth in tourism is ....

Listen and read

Is English Conquering the World?

9 **a)** [1.2] In 2002, an online talk radio station based in England broadcast an Internet discussion programme entitled 'Is English Conquering the World?' Following the programme, people were invited to send in their views to the website.

Read and / or listen to some of the voice mails, text messages and emails that people sent in. Tick (✓) the ones you think make a good point and (✗) the ones you disagree with.

You are in: BTR Online, 'Is English Conquering the World?'

Thursday, 23 August 2002. 10:50 GMT 11.50 UK

A I don't think there's a problem with English dominating the world. Everybody uses automobiles, don't they? As well as electricity and computers. Who cares where all these inventions come from? Everybody should use English. Who cares if it came from England?
Suraj, India

B There's a lot to be said for English as a lingua franca. But this doesn't necessarily mean it weakens other languages, and their speakers should retain full respect for their own tongue. After more than 25 years as an Englishman living in The Netherlands, I do not see that English is 'taking over', despite the obvious awareness of English and a liberal dose of it in spoken and written communication. On the contrary, Dutch remains a rich, living language with very much its own identity.
Philip Haskell, Rotterdam, Netherlands

C Speaking as an outsider, I hope and pray that all of you in Europe will hold on to your native languages as tightly as you can. I have studied Spanish, French, German and some Italian. There is such beauty in these languages, and each one allows expression in a different manner than the others. All throughout history, the dominant economic power has influenced the language of every other country. But the languages have rarely truly died.
Carrie, USA

D I think people should speak only two languages: one their mother tongue and the other English.
Shahid, Shikarpur, Pakistan

E Surely culture is about how one lives one's life, not the noises we make that is called language. Surely speaking one language – whether it be English or any other language – promotes greater understanding and breaks down barriers. Who really wants to live in a world of 2,000 languages? This makes communication with most of our fellow human beings impossible. Who cares whether it's English, German or Cantonese – the more of us who talk to one another, the better.
Paul O'Neill, N. Ireland

F 'Who wants to live in a world of 2,000 languages?' Well, I do for one!
Pat M. Thatcham, UK

G Originating from Ireland, I can tell you all that losing your own language kills your culture. When Ireland was swallowed up by Britain the Irish were put into an English-speaking school system. Result? The Irish language was 99% destroyed. And what is Irish culture now? Advertisements for Guinness? Lose your language = lose your soul. I am always being told that if it wasn't for the British I'd be speaking German. Well, if it wasn't for the British I'd be speaking Irish.
Brian Nolan, Ireland

H English is without doubt every European's native, second or third tongue. But I feel this will be a transitory cultural phenomenon. As soon as Eastern Asia rules by the strength of its economy – as the USA and the EU do at the moment – a standardised form of Chinese will emerge as a global language. It will be simplified from its current patterns no doubt, but no less universal than Latin or English were in their time.
Jenny, Hong Kong

b) Which text / texts:

1 equates English with other globally-used products and services? ...A...
2 celebrates the diversity of different languages? ....
3 advocates bilingualism? ....
4 directly contradicts the previous message? ....
5 suggests that the dominance of English will be short-lived? ....
6 is about the disappearance of a local language? ....
7 argues that the widespread use of English does not threaten local culture? ....
8 maintains that it is unimportant which local language we use? ....

Check your pronunciation

10 a) [1.3] Listen again to this extract from one of the texts. Pause at the points indicated and look at the *Pronunciation points* below.

There's a lot to be said for English as a lingua franca (1). But this doesn't necessarily mean it weakens other languages, and their speakers should retain full respect for their (2) own tongue. After more than 25 years as an Englishman living in The Netherlands, I do not see that English is 'taking over', despite the obvious (3) awareness of English and a liberal dose of it in spoken and written communication (4). On the contrary, Dutch remains a rich, living language with very much its own identity (5).
Philip Haskell, Rotterdam, Netherlands

LOOK!

Pronunciation points

1 Notice the 'weak' pronunciation of the letter 'a' in *as a*. This sound is known as the schwa (/ə/). Notice the same sound in the words *than*, *of* and *and* later in the text.

2 Notice the two ways *their* is pronounced in *their speakers* and *their own*. The final 'r' is only pronounced if the next word begins with a vowel sound.

3 Notice the pronunciation of *the* in *The Netherlands* and *the obvious*. The pronunciation of *the* changes when the next word begins with a vowel sound.

4 Notice the stress on *communication*. Words ending in *-ation* (such as *communication*, *education*, *immigration*) usually have the stress on the last-but-one syllable.

5 Notice the short /ɪ/ sound in *rich living*. This is also heard in *languages written*, and *its* and *identity*.

b) Practise reading the passage yourself, paying attention to the *Pronunciation points* above. Use the recording to help you if necessary.

Wordspot

world, earth, ground, floor

11 Complete the gaps with *world*, *earth*, *ground* or *floor*.

a Seventeen is far too young to get married. You have all the time in the .....world...... to find the right person.
b *Mario's* is the best restaurant in town. The pasta dishes are out of this ....
c That's life; one day you're depressed, the next day something cheers you up and you're on top of the ....
d With so many cheap flights on offer, you can go abroad and it needn't cost the ....
e I wouldn't criticise Peter's wife – he thinks the .... of her, you know.
f You could've killed someone! What on .... do you think you were doing?
g Internet cafés are now found in every country. They are truly a ....wide phenomenon.
h The idea for a new sports club was raised last year, but the idea never really got off the ....
i After staying out till 5am without telling his parents, Jeffrey was ....ed for a week.
j It was very foolish of the old man to keep all his money under the .... boards.
k Then came the .... -shattering news – the President had been assassinated.
l Florence certainly isn't shy. She was the first person on the dance ....
m Having won the championship at 17, it's important that Alvarez keeps his feet on the .... and doesn't think it's easy at the top.

Do you remember?

Pages 6-7

1 **What is the title of the module and what does the phrase mean?**

....

2 **What word is a synonym of *conflict*?** ....

3 **The words in bold are all in the plural form. Which of them cannot be used in the singular?**

a international **investors** b local **businesses**
c locally-produced **goods**
d communications **networks**

4 **What phrase means: *the amount of wealth, comfort and things that a particular group or country has*?**

....

5 **In the phrase *multi-ethnic*, what does the prefix *multi-* mean?** ....

6 **What is the noun form of the adjective *diverse*?**

....

Pages 8-9

7 **Which city is described in the reading text?**

....

8 **Which word in paragraph 1 means *holding tightly*?**

....

9 **What five things are most youngsters interested in, according to paragraph 2?** ....

....

....

10 **What word completes these compound nouns in paragraph 3?**

a shopping ....
b road ....
c housing ....

11 **What were considered 'unimaginable luxuries' in the 1980s?**

....

12 **Which adjective in paragraph 4 means:**

a very interesting? ....
b very beautiful? ....
c most important? ....

Pages 10-11

13 **Which sentence expresses annoyance?**

a He always does that.
b He's always doing that.

14 **According to the text *Did you know ...?*, approximately how many people speak English as their first language?** ....

15 **What proportion of the data on the world's computers is in English?**

a 8 % b 80 % c 88 %

16 **What did the word *nice* mean 500 years ago?**

....

17 **Which of the words below does not have a plural form?**

a idiom b noun c information

18 **What was the name of the expert on international English?** ....

Pages 12-13

19 **The task is to devise an** ....

20 **What two reasons for learning English are listed in section 1a) of the questionnaire?**

....

....

21 **What word describes a dictionary which does not include translations?** ....

22 **Correct the spelling of these words.**

a questionaire ....
b confidant (adj) ....
c pronounciation ....

23 **Four verbs combine with English in the *Learner questionnaire* on page 13. What are they?**

....

....

24 **On what pages of the Students' Book can you find the contents page?** ....

Pages 14-15

25 **What floor can you find at the bottom of the sea?**

....

26 **Which is a way of describing shocking and important news or events: *earth-breaking*, *earth-shattering* or *earth-smashing*?** ....

27 **If you're *grounded* what are you not allowed to do?** ....

28 **What are *floorboards* made of?** ....

29 **Where do you keep your feet if you are realistic about what you can do and not overly ambitious?**

....

30 **What word on page 15 means: *a very heavy shower of rain*?** ....

module 2

Vocabulary

How would *you* feel?

1 **a)** Find fifteen adjectives for describing feelings in the word box below.

T	H	R	E	L	I	E	V	E	D	W	I	F	C
A	P	P	R	E	H	E	N	S	I	V	E	L	A
T	T	O	P	L	E	T	D	O	W	N	L	A	A
D	F	T	D	H	E	F	E	F	T	Y	S	B	O
E	U	D	E	P	R	E	S	S	E	D	I	B	V
T	R	G	L	R	A	N	P	R	O	U	D	E	E
E	I	D	I	I	N	S	E	C	U	R	E	R	R
R	O	E	G	S	T	C	R	O	S	S	O	G	J
M	U	F	H	E	N	T	A	A	P	A	T	A	O
I	S	C	T	N	T	W	T	A	I	T	T	S	Y
N	A	S	E	T	P	O	E	S	O	R	R	T	E
E	T	H	D	R	H	O	R	R	I	F	I	E	D
D	I	S	I	L	L	U	S	I	O	N	E	D	O

b) Write the correct adjective next to the definition.

1 A*pprehensive*...... worried or nervous about something that is going to happen
2 C..................... angry or annoyed
3 D..................... very pleased and happy
4 D..................... very unhappy over a long period
5 D..................... in a very bad situation, almost without hope
6 D..................... unhappy because you have lost your belief in something
7 D..................... very sure that you are going to do something, even if others disagree
8 F..................... very, very surprised
9 F..................... extremely angry
10 H..................... upset because you find something very shocking
11 I..................... not feeling confident about yourself or your situation in life
12 L..................... D..................... disappointed by something or someone
13 O..................... extremely happy about something
14 P..................... pleased at your own or other people's achievements
15 R..................... pleased because something you were worried about didn't happen

What makes you laugh?

2 Match the words in the box below to the correct definition.

anecdote epigram sketch cartoon limerick slapstick ~~comic book~~ pun stand-up comedian corny punch line witty

a ...*comic book*..... *n* [C] a magazine, often for children, that tells a story using cartoons

b .... *n* [C] 1 a funny drawing in a newspaper, often including humorous remarks about news events 2 a short film that is made by photographing a series of drawings

c .... *adj* using words in a clever and amusing way

d .... *n* [U] humorous acting in which the performers fall over, throw things, etc.

e .... *n* [C] someone who tells jokes and funny stories in front of an audience

f .... *n* [C] a short humorous scene which is part of a longer show

g .... *n* [C] the last few lines of a joke or story that make it funny or interesting

h .... *n* [C] an amusing story which is based on one's own personal experience

i .... *adj* not new, interesting or original

j .... *n* [C] a short sentence that expresses an idea in a clever and amusing way

k .... *n* [C] an amusing use of a word or phrase that has two meanings, or of words with the same sound but different meanings

l .... *n* [C] a humorous short poem with three long lines and two short ones

Grammar: perfect verb forms

General

3 Complete the sentences with an appropriate perfect form of the verb in brackets.

a Chris ....*has been talking*..... (talk) to that girl for ages. I wonder what it is that's so interesting.
b The woman at the party seemed to recognise me, though I couldn't remember .... (meet) her before.
c If you don't hurry up, they .... (eat) all the food by the time we get there.
d Bill .... (be) depressed ever since he lost his job last year.
e Suzanne .... (drive) for just a few weeks when she had her first accident.
f Nearly half a million people are believed .... (leave) their homes as a result of the disaster.
g Although it was my first visit for many years, I was surprised by how much the city .... (change).
h It's very hard for me to comment, never .... (read) the book myself.
i Ramsey never revealed to the police where he .... (hide) the money.
j Life .... (be) much quieter since Tom left home.
k What's the matter with Kate? She .... (lie) on her bed all day, staring out of the window.
l Next week is my first anniversary: I .... (work) in this department for exactly a year.
m They ought .... (check) the weather forecast before setting out on such a dangerous journey.
n The roads were all flooded: it .... (rain) heavily for nearly ten hours.
o So far today, I .... (receive) over 30 emails. How will I get time to answer them all?

Present Perfect Simple and Continuous

4 Complete the sentences using the Present Perfect Simple or Present Perfect Continuous.

a Apparently, Robert ....*has had*..... (have) an accident – he's on his way to hospital right now.
b How long .... (you look) for a new job?
c I .... (wait) for the phone to ring all morning. I can't stand it any more!
d .... (you ever play) baseball?
e I know why Julian looks so tired – he .... (work) too hard recently.
f Neil .... (never do) anything like this before in all the time I've known him.
g You .... (watch) videos for over three hours now: it's about time you found something else to do.
h I .... (never see) Carla looking so depressed.
i It's no secret that Steven and Monika .... (see) each other for several months now.
j I .... (try) to get in touch with Jerry all morning, but I .... (not have) any luck yet.
k I .... (never understand) why people aren't prepared to queue up in a civilised manner.
l I .... (wait) for the taxi for the last twenty-five minutes. Why .... (it / not arrive) yet?

Past Perfect Simple and Continuous

5 Match the beginnings with the endings.

a Paul went to bed
b Her eyes were red,
c It was a shock to realise
d By the time Roger retired
e I'd never believed in love at first sight
f Paula and James had only been going out for a month
g She found it difficult to drive in Scotland,
h Having already told the police what I'd seen,

1 he'd been lying all along.
2 when they decided to get married.
3 as soon as he'd finished his report.
4 but I don't think it was because she'd been peeling onions.
5 I didn't think it necessary to tell them again.
6 until I met you.
7 he had achieved most of his ambitions.
8 never having driven on the left before.

a ..*3*.... b .... c .... d .... e ....
f .... g .... h ....

Present / Past Perfect Simple and Continuous

6 Complete the gaps by putting the verb in brackets into the correct tense: Present Perfect Simple or Present Perfect Continuous.

Fancy That!

1 A horse and a sheep were walking past a bar one sunny day.
'Fancy a cold drink?' said the horse.
'(1) I *'ve been pulling* (pull) a cart all day, and
5 it's thirsty work, I can tell you.'
The sheep (2) .... (sit) in a field all afternoon, with no protection from the sun: the only thing he (3) .... (have)
10 to drink all day was filthy water. 'I know what you mean,' he said. 'I (4) .... (think) about a cold glass of beer since about 12 o'clock.' So they went inside. The horse ordered two beers and reached over for the menu. 'I fancy
15 something to eat as well,' he said. 'I (5) .... (eat) ten sacks of oats so far this week, and I'm just about sick of them. I don't think my owner (6) .... (hear) of a balanced
20 diet.'
'Too right,' said the sheep. 'I need a change too. I fancy a burger. (7) .... (you / try) the burgers here?'
The horse replied that it was the first time he
25 (8) ....(eat) there too, but he decided to have the same, with extra cheese. Then he remembered he (9) .... (not / go) to the lavatory all day, and he needed to go urgently.
30 'Any idea where the lavatory is?' he asked his friend.
'No. I don't.'
Just then, a dog who (10) .... (sit) at a nearby table came over and said: 'Please
35 forgive me, but I (11) .... (listen) to your conversation, and I can tell you that the lavatory is downstairs, on your left.'
The sheep turned to the horse with an amazed look on his face.
40 'Fancy that! I (12) .... (never / see) a talking dog before!'

Patterns to notice

Cleft sentences

7 Put the words in the correct order to make a cleft sentence.

a to do / must / is / we / What / stay calm / all try
What we must all try to do is stay calm.

b started / the demonstrators / It / who / the trouble / wasn't
....
....

c only / It / last week / that / was / she finally / got in touch
....
....

d like / we / about Australia / What / the marvellous / is / weather
....
....

e that / only / you can park / after 6.30 / It's / for free / here
....
....

f do / should / now / is / What / get / rest / you / plenty of
....
....

g I realised / It / I got home / only / that / I'd picked up / was / the wrong coat / when
....
....

h like / is / living / traffic / here / the awful / What / I don't / about
....
....

i a barbecue / having / suggested / wasn't / It / who / me
....
....

j annoys / is / really / What / to us / you lied / the way / me
....
....

Pronunciation

How sentence stress changes meaning

8 **a)** [2.1] Listen to the sentence below with 'neutral' stress. Which words are stressed?

Charlie Jones has been at home for five days.

b) [2.2] If we put stress on particular words, the meaning can change. Listen to these examples.

1 **Charlie** Jones has been at home for five days (not **Heather** Jones).
2 Charlie **Jones** has been at home for five days (not Charlie **Smith**).
3 Charlie Jones **has** been at home for five days (we thought he **hadn't**).
4 Charlie Jones has been at **home** for five days (not at **school**).
5 Charlie Jones has been at home for **five** days (not **ten** days).
6 Charlie Jones has been at home for five **days** (not five **weeks**).

c) Practise saying the six sentences.

d) [2.3] Listen to the sentences on the recording. Circle the most logical way to continue them.

1 It's getting easier to get American films here ...
  a but getting books is still a problem.
  (b) but it's hard to find English ones.
  c not more difficult.
2 Peter was busy working the last time I looked ...
  a but I'm not sure if he is now.
  b not watching TV. c but Henry wasn't.
3 Christiane is playing rugby on Saturday ...
  a after all. b not Sunday. c not watching it.
4 Is Barbara's engagement party this weekend ...
  a or next weekend? b or her birthday party?
  c or did she cancel it?
5 Monica is coming to the conference tomorrow ...
  a but her husband can't make it. b not today.
  c she's managed to cancel her meeting.
6 In 2002, the financial situation seemed to be improving ...
  a but in fact it was getting worse.
  b but the military situation was getting worse.
  c but now it's getting worse.
7 Internet cafés are opening all over our city now ...
  a how about where you live?
  b but a lot of traditional cafés are closing.
  c but it'll be different in a year's time.
8 We're going out for dinner this evening ...
  a we're not eating at home.
  b How about you?
  c not tomorrow night.

Listen and read

Limericks

A limerick is a short, humorous poem, often nonsensical, with five lines – three long and two short – which usually begins *There once was a* ... They first became popular nearly 200 hundred years ago. By the way, Limerick is a city in the south-west of Ireland – but nobody seems to be sure quite what the connection is!

9 **a)** [2.4] Listen to and / or read the limericks.

Limericks

1

There once was a student named Bessor
Whose knowledge grew lesser and lesser
It at last grew so small
He knew nothing at all
And now he's a college professor

2

There once was a man from Blackheath
Who sat on his pair of false teeth
He said, with a start[1]
'Oh dear! Bless my heart!
I've bitten myself underneath!'

3

There once was a baker named Fred
Whose success didn't go to his head
Instead of just looking
He ate all his cooking
So it went to his waistline instead

4

There was a young girl from Berlin
Who was so uncommonly thin
That when she essayed[2]
To drink lemonade
She slipped through the straw and fell in

5

There once was a lady from Hyde
Who ate 20 green apples and died
While her lover lamented
The apples fermented
And made cider inside her inside

6
A gentleman dining at Crewe
Found a very large mouse in his stew
Said the waiter, 'Don't shout
And wave it about
Or the others will all want one too.'

7
There was a young fellow from Leeds
Who swallowed six packets of seeds
It soon came to pass
He was covered in grass
And he couldn't sit down for the weeds

8
There was a young lady named Bright
Whose speed was far faster than light
She set off one day
In a relative way
And came back the previous night

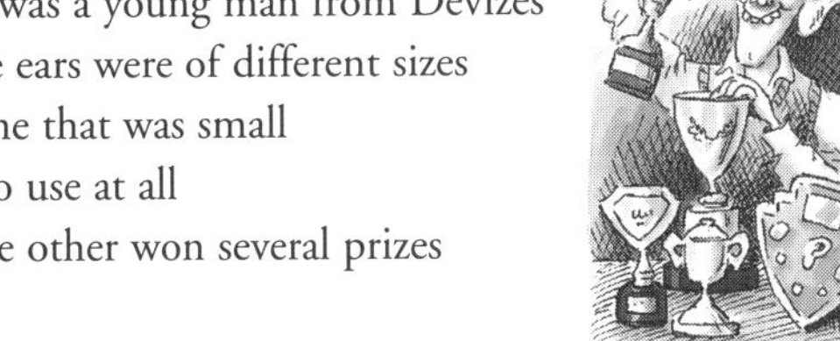

9
There was a young man from Devizes
Whose ears were of different sizes
The one that was small
Was no use at all
But the other won several prizes

10
There was a young man from Japan
Whose limericks would never quite scan[3]
Asked why this was so
He said 'I don't know,
I think it's because I have a tendency to try to put as many words into the last line as I possibly can.'

[1] a sudden movement of fear or surprise
[2] a formal word meaning *tried*
[3] to have a regular rhythm

b) Which one do you think is:
the easiest?
the strangest?
the cleverest?
the funniest?

Check your pronunciation

10 a) [2.5] Listen to the recording of limerick 6 again. Notice how stressed words make a rhythm.

● ● ●
A gentleman dining at Crewe
● ● ● ●
Found a very large mouse in his stew
● ● ●
Said the waiter, 'Don't shout
● ●
And wave it about
● ● ●
Or the others will all want one too.'

b) [2.6] Listen to the stressed words on the recording. Try to say them in time with the rhythm.

c) Listen again to the recording of limerick 6. Pause at the points indicated and look at the *Pronunciation points* below.

A gentleman (1) dining at Crewe
Found a very large mouse in his stew (2)
Said the waiter, 'Don't shout (3)
And wave (4) it about
Or the others (5) will all want one too.

LOOK!

Pronunciation points

1. Notice that the word *gentleman* is pronounced with the stress on the first syllable, followed by two schwa /ə/ sounds.
2. Notice the pronunciation of the word *stew* /stjuː/: the last sound rhymes with *Crewe* /kruː/ in the previous line.
3. Notice the /aʊ/ sound in *shout*. The same sound is heard in *found*, *mouse* (line 2) and *about* (line 4)
4. Notice the /eɪ/ sound in *wave*. The same sound is heard in *waiter* (line 3)
5. Notice the way that the 'e' in *the* is pronounced /iː/ because it comes before a vowel sound and is connected to *others* with a /j/ sound.

d) Practise reading the limerick, paying attention to the rhythm and the *Pronunciation points* above. Use the recording to help you if necessary.

Wordspot

Idioms with *laugh*, *cry* and *tears*

11 Complete the sentences with one of the phrases from the box below.

no laughing matter	the last laugh	floods of tears
shoulder to cry on	crying her eyes out	
burst out laughing	bored to tears	close to tears
burst into tears	~~laughed my head off~~	

a When I saw the photos of my father as a teenager, I ..*laughed my head off*...: he looked so ridiculous with long hair.

b People don't always take the problem of athlete's foot seriously, but it's ...., I can tell you.

c After the break-up of his marriage, Dan's best friend was always there when he needed a ....

d Petra had expected her father to be angry or upset when he saw her hair dyed orange; instead he ....

e I don't usually get emotional watching films, but at the end of *The Lion King* my daughter and I were in ....

f As a child, Eva was often teased because she was so skinny. But she certainly had .... : she's now a millionaire supermodel.

g It was heartbreaking to see the little child .... because her doll was broken.

h The show lasted nearly four hours: from the expression on people's faces, it was clear that many of the audience were ....

i Many people at the funeral were crying openly. Even those who didn't know her seemed to be ....

j As Irena received her gold medal, she unexpectedly .... The emotion of victory had finally caught up with her.

Check your writing

Linking words and phrases (1)

12 **a)** Circle the phrase a), b) or c) which has the same meaning as the word or phrase in bold.

1 The audience was impatient and rather lethargic. **However**, the atmosphere changed when the singer appeared.
a Although b Whenever (c)But

2 People were on their feet, **as if** pulled by a mysterious force.
a as though b like c since

3 **As well as** the originals, she performed an array of cover versions.
a Apart from b In addition to c Including

4 But **whatever** she sang, it was clear that Gray was giving 100%.
a however b no matter what c until

5 When the band **finally** launched into *I Try* ...
a at last b at the end c lastly

6 There are traces of other influences too, **such as** Nina Simone and Tina Turner.
a as b as if c like

7 **Yet** in the end, Macy Gray sounds like no one but herself.
a Already b Always c But

8 Other tracks **which** deserve a mention are the smoky ballad *Still*, ...
a that b what c who

b) Use one of the words or phrases above to complete the sentences.

1 The group's first two albums were hugely successful: ....*however*....., the third album, *Cloudburst*, was much less well-received.

2 .... kind of music you like, you'll find something to please you on this album.

3 Her face was pale and ill-looking, ... she had been without sleep for several days.

4 These days, few people remember Bill Haley. .... his place in the history of music is assured.

5 He has toured with many of the world's best known singers, ... Britney Spears and Shania Twain.

6 .... her recent hit *Harvest Moon*, the new album includes three songs she wrote herself.

7 The Rolling Stones' latest tour, ... begins in Toronto next month, is rumoured to be their last.

8 The audience had waited nearly two hours: when the band .... appeared, the reception was not entirely friendly.

Do you remember?

Pages 16-17

1 **Rearrange the letters to make three words meaning *very happy*.**
a didlegeth .... b daplese ....
c ojorveedy ....

2 **Which of these does not mean *angry*?**
a cross b flabbergasted c furious

3 **What are the missing vowels in the following words?**
a d_sp_r_t_ b d_s_ll_s__n_d
c d_t_rm_n_d

4 **What does the phrasal verb *turn up* mean?**
....

5 **What idiom means: *to get very high marks in an examination or test*?**
....

6 **What idiom with *blue* means *completely unexpectedly*?** ....

Pages 18-19

7 **When you are listening to a joke, when do you hear the punchline?** ....

8 **Which of the three sentences is correct?**
a I have made a bet with my friends that I can make you say at least three words.
b I have been making a bet with my friends that I can make you say at least three words.
c I have made a bet with my friends that I can make you to say at least three words.

9 **Where did the man who dreamed about eating his shoe come from?** ....

10 **What three adjectives does Basil use to describe Mrs Richards (to himself)?**
....

11 **According to Oscar Wilde, history would have been different if who had learned to laugh?**
....

12 **What form of the verb *to be* is found in the phrase *to have been happy*?** ....

Pages 20-21

13 **Name two things that can go wrong if you appear in public.**
....
....

14 **The two sentences below have the same meaning. What is the missing word in sentence b)?**
a I didn't invite them.
b It wasn't .... who invited them.

15 **Which is the correct preposition?**
What I really like *about* / *from* / *of* my city is the nice weather.

16 **What word is missing from the two idioms below?**
.... out laughing .... into tears.

17 **If you are proved to be right in the end, you have the last what?** ....

18 **What can you be *close to, bored to* or *in floods of*?**
....

Pages 22-23

19 **Which word from the *Useful language box* is spelt incorrectly?**
a ashamed b desperate c mistified
....

20 **Complete the time phrases with the correct preposition.**
a .... this time
b .... that point
c from that day ....

21 **What phrasal verb with *go* means *to pass* and is used to talk about time?** ....

22 **What word means *extremely hungry?*** ....

23 **Which preposition follows the verb *beg*?**
....

24 **If a story is *touching*, does it make you feel sad or does it make you laugh?** ....

Pages 24-25

25 **What nationality is the songwriter Smokey Robinson?** ....

26 **Whose concert is reviewed on page 25 and where did it take place?** ....

27 **How many people were there in her band?**
....

28 **What idiomatic phrase means: *to do something with maximum effort*?** ....

29 **What is the title of the album reviewed?**
....

30 **What do the following adjectives describe?**
wonderful sugar sweet harsh scratchy
....

module 3

Vocabulary

The right way to behave

1 Use the clues to complete the puzzle. The number of letters and part of speech are given in brackets.

1 To touch someone lightly (e.g. on the back) with the palm of your hand. (3, *verb*)
2 To go red in the face, often because you're embarrassed. (5, *verb*)
3 A quality that makes people like you and feel attracted to you. (5, *noun*)
4 To use offensive words, e.g. when you are angry. (5, *verb*)
5 A way of saying things so that people are not hurt or offended. (7, *adjective*)
6 A quiet laugh, like a child's, often out of nerves or embarrassment. (6, *verb / noun*)
7 To use religious or holy words in a way that offends people's religious beliefs. (9, *verb*)
8 A remark that tells someone they have done well or look nice. (10, *noun*)
9 Difficult, embarrassing or inconvenient. (7, *adjective*)
10 Honest, even if this means upsetting people. The opposite of *sharp*. (5, *adjective*)
11 Ways of behaving in a social situation. They can be good or bad. (7, *noun*)
12 Something that cannot be mentioned or discussed. (5, *noun / adjective*)
13 The formal rules for polite behaviour in a particular situation. (9, *noun*)
14 Feeling ashamed, nervous and uncomfortable. (11, *adjective*)
15 Showing no awareness of other people's feelings. (5, *adjective*)
16 Not polite. Likely to offend people. (4, *adjective*)
17 To open your mouth wide because you are tired or bored. (4, *verb / noun*)
18 Discriminating against one sex in favour of the other. (6, *adjective*)
19 A colloquial word meaning unreliable or untrustworthy. (5, *adjective*)
20 Expect people to say *Bless You!* or *Gesundheit!* when you do this. (6, *verb / noun*)

				1 P	A	T				
					2 B			S		
					3 C			R		
					D					
			4 S		E					
	5 T		C		F					
			6 G		G			E		
7	L		S		H			E		
8	O		P		I			N		
					J					
			9 A		K			R		
				10	L			T		
					M					
			11 M		N			R		
		12	A		O					
					P					
		13	T		Q			T		
14	M		A		R			S		
		15	R		S					
					T					
				16	U					
					V					
			17 Y		W					
			18 S		X			T		
	19		D		Y					
	20		E		Z					

2 Complete the sentences using the correct form of a word from Exercise 1.

a One of the members of the audience seemed to be deliberately asking ...*awkward*... questions – I must say I found some of them very hard to deal with!
b Nobody was brave enough to laugh out loud, but I thought I heard someone .... at the back of the class.
c I found out that I was using the women's toilet by mistake – I can't tell you how .... I felt!
d What I'm about to say may well upset people, but you all know I have the reputation of being extremely ....
e I'm never coming back to this restaurant again! The waiters were so ....
f After a night without sleep, it was very difficult to stop myself .... in class the following day.
g Sex, religion and death are often considered .... subjects when it comes to class discussions.
h One of the best ways to put someone in a good mood is to pay them a .... about how nice they look.
i Although he was angry, it was silly of Kelly to .... at the referee: fortunately for Kelly, I don't think the referee heard him!
j I've always thought that parents should make it a priority to teach their children good .... : how they behave in public is so important.
k My dog really likes people: it makes him very happy if you .... him on the back.
l It was .... of you to bring up the topic of divorce. Don't you know that Gaby's husband has just left her?
m I'm sorry ... I seem to have caught a cold in the nose and I just can't stop ....
n Many people .... when they're asked a personal question. Unfortunately, there's no way of controlling the rush of blood to your face.
o It's definitely .... of you to insist that the new secretary has to be female.
p There are very complicated rules of .... concerning what you are allowed to say or do when you're introduced to a member of the Royal Family.
q What we have to try and do is to find a .... way of telling Peter that he doesn't have enough experience for the job.
r There are some very .... characters hanging around in this bar. Let's finish our drinks and move on somewhere else.
s Lisa uses all her .... to get people to do what she wants – you won't be able to resist.
t The church says it finds the film of Christ's life offensive. It contains ....

3 **a)** Match the adjectives with the nouns to form eight combinations found in the text *Perfect Behaviour in an Imperfect World* on pages 28–29 of the Students' Book.

1 uneasy	a attention
2 public	b generation
3 social	c girlfriend
4 former	d manners
5 the older	e liar
6 mobile	f silence
7 undivided	g situation
8 bad	h transport
9 complete	i phone

b) Write a sentence showing the meaning of each of the phrases.

There was an uneasy silence when George told his parents he was going to drop out of school.

Word building

4 Complete the sentences on the right by changing the word in capitals to the correct form (noun, adjective, etc.). If necessary, use a good monolingual dictionary (e.g. *The Longman Dictionary of Contemporary English*) to help you.

Before you write your answer, check the following points.

- Think about what kind of word is required (noun, adjective, etc.) e.g. *tradition* (noun) → *traditional* (adjective).
- In many cases, there may be more than one noun / adjective, etc. Check the dictionary definition to make sure you get the right one. (e.g. *immigrant* / *immigration*).
- Think about whether you need to add a prefix (e.g. *un-*, *over-*, *under-*).

Modern Manners

Once upon a time it was considered (1) .*gentlemanly*.. for men to open doors for women – but nowadays there's a danger that the gesture might actually be (2) .... Is it (3) .... to suggest that a woman is incapable of opening the door for herself? **GENTLEMAN** **INTERPRET** **ACCEPT**

For many Asian people, blowing your nose in public is seen not only as (4) .... – just think of all those germs flying into the air – but as something which is actually (5) .... : so if in doubt ... sniff! **HYGIENE** **OFFEND**

Is it OK for teachers to wear jeans and a T-shirt to class? Teachers who want to create the (6) .... that they are relaxed and approachable might think so, but some students do consider it (7) .... to come to class casually dressed, and such a casual attitude might even be seen as (8) .... to those students who expect their teachers to dress smartly. **IMPRESS** **PROFESSION** **RESPECT**

Grammar: modals

Mixed modals

5 Which of the phrases in the box below could replace the phrases in bold in the text without changing the meaning?

am unable to	am unwilling to
are sometimes	will possibly
was unable to	perhaps went
perhaps you are	is it OK to
refuses to	
is not the correct thing to	
I'm absolutely sure you are	
are able to	~~it's advisable to~~
I feel it is necessary to	
It would've been a good idea for you to have	
Is it possible for you to	

Neither a Borrower nor a Lender be

1 Borrowing and lending money is a sticky subject. Where large sums of money are concerned, (1) **you should** always try to be businesslike about it, but (2) **I must** warn you that such transactions (3) **can be** absolutely fatal to friendships. Always consider the worst scenario, 'What if I (4) **can't** pay her
5 back? What if she (5) **won't** repay me?' If you (6) **can**, borrow from a bank. It's much less embarrassing, even though it (7) **might** cost you a bit more. With smaller sums, (8) **you may be** one of those people who is vague about these things ... In fact, with the advent of automatic cash machines this really (9) **shouldn't** happen. Only a few years ago, if you'd missed the bank
10 by 3.30 on a Friday a typical conversation (10) **might've gone** something like this:
'My dear, dear friend (11), **may I** ask you an enormous favour?'
'Of course ... anything.'
'(12) **Would you** be so kind as to lend me £20 ... just till Monday?'
15 '£20?! No I certainly (13) **will not**! (14) **You must be** out of your mind. Are you telling me you're broke again?'
'No, it's just that I got to the bank late and so I (15) **couldn't** get any money out.'
'Well, (16) **you should've** got there earlier. Serves you right.'
20 Better to avoid such embarrassment, eh?

Semi-modals

6 Rewrite the following sentences using the appropriate form of *ought to*, *need to* or *have to*.

a The restaurant accepted euros, so it wasn't necessary to change our money.
The restaurant accepted euros, so we didn't have to change our money.

b It would've been a good idea for us to check the train times before we set out.
....

c It's not necessary to book tickets in advance: you can just turn up on the day.
....

d It was unnecessary for you to take so much trouble ... but thanks anyway!
....

e Was it necessary for you to pay for the whole week, or can we pay day-by-day?
....

f Your suit should be cleaned as soon as possible.
....

g It wasn't necessary to pay for our meals. They were included in the price of the holiday.
....

h It would be a good idea for you to buy some mosquito repellent for your holiday
....

i Do you think it's advisable for us to take some food for the journey?
....

j It's not necessary to get a visa if you're only staying for a week.
....

7 Complete the sentences with an appropriate form of the verb *dare*.

a Martin ...*daren't*..... tell Lizzie that he's desperately in love with her in case she laughs in his face.

b Because we were all so afraid of her, we .... tell Suzanna that she'd made a mistake.

c Don't .... threaten me again! I'll call the police!

d I .... tell Lucy what's really happened to her pet goldfish – she'd be terribly upset.

e How .... suggest that I lied to your parents!

f It's his first holiday abroad, but I .... say he's old enough to look after himself.

Pronunciation

Rhyming sounds

8 **a)** Circle the two words that rhyme with the modal verb in bold.

1	**might**	(bite)	straight	(white)	wait
2	**could**	cold	ruled	wood	stood
3	**need**	we'd	lid	beard	read (present)
4	**dare**	far	their	wear	here
5	**ought**	caught	note	sort	out
6	**can't**	ant	aren't	want	aunt

b) [3.1] Listen and check. Practise saying the rhyming words, copying the voices on the recordings.

Patterns to notice

Abstract nouns followed by relative clauses

9 Complete the sentences with *why*, *where* or *which*.

a Nobody really knows the reason ......*why*...... Teresa decided to cancel the wedding.

b Recently, there have been a number of cases .... our security measures have proved ineffective.

c The 1990s was a period in .... being computer-literate became more and more important in the job market.

d I absolutely loved the film *Angry Sky*. The part .... the hero returns home had me in floods of tears!

e I am not at all satisfied about the way in .... our complaint was dealt with.

f I really can't see .... children shouldn't be allowed in the garden.

g It was one of those situations .... nobody can really be blamed.

h Nobody can be completely sure about the extent to .... people are influenced by what they read in the newspapers.

i Things with our neighbours have got so bad, we've reached the point .... we've thought about moving house.

Listen and read

Nosey Questions

10 **a)** [3.2] Read and / or listen to the text below. Where do you think it comes from?

1 a book giving advice for people visiting the UK for the first time
2 the advice column of a teenage magazine
3 a book of humorous articles
4 a book of advice about social etiquette.

Nosey QUESTIONS

If someone you know asks you nosey questions then you are not obliged to answer if you don't want to. Here it is more important that you have some polite brush-off[1] but it is still not rude for you to refuse and it would be rude for the other person to press you.

If you think they shouldn't have asked the question ('How much money do you earn?', 'Are you pregnant yet?', 'Are you and John still in love?') then I strongly recommend looking very shocked and saying 'I can't believe you just asked me that!' and either leaving them to stumble out of it or moving on yourself to another, perhaps related, subject. If they try to press you, as opposed to defending themselves lamely and saying 'I was just interested ...', then you can keep the shocked look and say 'I'm not telling you that' with as much emphasis as you like on the 'you'.

But what if the question isn't quite so unforgivable? You don't want to answer it ('How much did you pay for that?', 'Are you having a relationship with him?', 'Where did you buy that?' – these are strictly subjective examples by the way: you can decide for yourself what questions go into what categories). Or supposing the really awful question came from someone you don't feel you can be too hard on (elderly relative, boss). Then you need a more smiling response: 'I can't possibly tell you that' or 'I'm not telling anyone that' or 'Wouldn't you like to know?' or 'That's none of your business'. Any of these *if said with a cheerful face* should get you out of it. As ever, if people press, then they have lost the right to a polite answer. Some people really don't understand why you won't tell them. 'But I'd tell *you*', they say. You must just answer 'I never tell anyone that kind of thing' until they get the message. But you must stand firm, because otherwise they'll never learn and will keep expecting you to tell them your innermost secrets. There is certainly never any need to tell your secrets just because someone else told theirs.

There are questions that seem perfectly reasonable – 'Are you planning to move?', 'Are you going to go back to work?', 'Are you going on holiday this year?' – but if answered truthfully might lead to minefields or unexpected (and maybe unwanted) revelations of bankruptcy, pregnancy, redundancy, divorce, etc. Here you are free to tell white lies and say 'We don't know / haven't decided yet / haven't really thought about it'. Looking vague and serene and changing the subject is the key here. You generally find that people did leap to conclusions, but they were the wrong ones ('I was convinced that meant you were getting married, not splitting up') and nothing to worry about. If the question was reasonable then it's polite to embarrass the asker as little as possible – they were probably only making conversation in the first place.

[1] *A clear sign that you don't wish to speak to someone.*

b) Read the text again and circle nine nosey questions and underline the ten suggested answers.

Checking your pronunciation

11 **a)** [3.3] Listen again to this extract from the text. Pause at the points indicated and look at the *Pronunciation points* below.

> 1 If you think they shouldn't have (1) asked the question ('How much money do you earn?'(2), 'Are you pregnant yet?', 'Are you
> 5 and John still in love?')(3) then I strongly recommend looking very shocked and saying 'I can't believe you just asked me that!'(4) and either leaving them
> 10 to stumble out of it or moving on yourself to another, perhaps related, subject. If they try to press you, as opposed to defending themselves lamely and
> 15 saying 'I was just interested ...', then you can keep the shocked look and say 'I'm not telling you that'(5) with as much emphasis as you like on the 'you'.

Pronunciation points LOOK!

1 Notice the pronunciation of *shouldn't have* as one word /ʃədntəv/.

2 Notice that the voice goes down at the end of the question *How much money do you earn?* as with most *wh-* questions.

3 Notice that the voice goes up at the end of the questions *Are you pregnant yet?* and *Are you and John still in love?* as with most *Yes / No* questions.

4 Notice how the speaker expresses shock in *I can't believe you just asked me that!*

5 Notice the strong stress on *you* in *I'm not telling **you** that.*

b) Practise reading the passage yourself, paying attention to the *Pronunciation points* above. Use the recording to help you if necessary.

Check your writing

Punctuation

LOOK!

1 Apostrophe (')
Apostrophes are used:
- for possession:
  ... today's way of conducting business
- to replace missing letters:
  it's not a computer you're talking to
- when we quote: *... overused clichés like 'Please find attached herewith'*

2 Dash (–)
The dash is used in informal writing before a list or explanation, or instead of a semi-colon:
... a deep depression – he refuses to look for a job or go back to college

3 Brackets ( )
Brackets (also called *parentheses*) are used before and after an explanation which could be removed from the sentence:
FYI (For Your Information)

4 Exclamation mark (!)
Exclamation marks are used to convey excitement:
We won!

5 Slash (/)
The slash is used between two or more words which are alternatives:
first I have to look in my office / husband's / other diary

12 Punctuate the following lines from different email messages. The number of punctuation marks needed is shown in brackets.

a We have asked Mr. Lawley the companys Chief Executive Officer if he would care to attend. (3)
b Please feel free to bring your husband wife partner ... and anyone else who youd like to share our party (4)
c Hi everyone Im currently doing a class project on famous French painters mine is someone called Braque and I wondered if anyone out there had any information about him her. Thanks (6)
d I was round at my friend Saras house the other day guess what she told me (3)
e Its no surprise that the new exhibition has been described by Theo Landis New Yorks leading art critic as remarkable. (6)
f Sorry I havent got round to answering you know how busy it can get at this time of year (3)

Do you remember?

Pages 26-27

1 According to Matthew Engel, what should be taught in schools? ....

2 Something which is extreme or excessive can be described as .... ***the top.***

3 Which of these words is the closest in meaning to *difficult / embarrassing*?

a awkward b familiar c revolting
d offensive

4 Supply the correct prefix to complete the words.

a _ _ hygienic (not hygienic)
b _ _ professional (not professional)
c _ _ _ interpret (interpret wrongly)

5 What phrasal verb means: *to make an informal visit to someone's house*? ....

6 What three things shouldn't you do without putting your hand over your mouth?

....

Pages 28-29

7 What does one writer dislike being *turned into someone else's telephone box*? ....

8 What does one girl want her boyfriend to remove from his flat? ....

9 What did one unfortunate person have stuck between their teeth? ....

10 According to John Morgan, what does a *double diary device* allow you to do?

....

11 In the sentence: *Why not have some shots taken of yourself and leave them lying around*, what does *shots* mean? ....

12 What *drops* in the idiom meaning you finally understand something? ....

Pages 30-31

13 In the sentence: *Many young people these days just won't accept the importance of good manners*, what does *won't* mean? ....

14 Which of these modal verbs cannot normally be used to make a request for permission?

a can b could c may d must e should

15 What was the modal verb in this sentence?

You .... be Karina's mother, surely? You're far too young.

16 In the survey, what percentage of people said that they were *chronically shy*?

a 10 % b 25 % c 40 % d 65 %

17 Complete the sentence with *wh-* words.

People often have problems communicating in situations (1) .... they're unsure of (2) .... they're speaking to. A lot depends on the way in (3) .... you say it.

18 What phrase means: *to become quieter after you have been excited or emotional*?

....

Pages 32-33

19 In the sentence: *The main thing to get across is ...* , what does *get across* mean?

a to communicate b to find c to understand

20 What did Richard do after he failed his exams?

....

21 In the idiom meaning: *to suddenly become very angry*, what do you *fly off*? ....

22 What kind of company does Anna work for?

....

23 Who is *the flatmate from hell*? ....

24 Rearrange the letters of two adjectives describing Julia.

a bit lostpi and helfiss in all sorts of small ways

....

Pages 34-35

25 How is the growth of email described?

a exploded b exploding c explosive
d explosion

26 What do the letters FYI and BTW mean ?

....

27 Which of these words are incorrectly spelt?

a courrier b receive c extremely
d herewhith e punctuation

28 What city is Lucia moving to soon?

....

29 Write down three phrases which can be used for agreeing to do something.

....

30 Rearrange the letters to make adjectives used to describe someone's attitude.

a etilpo .... b asucal ....
c trucental ....
d epotovacier ....

module 4

Vocabulary

Body and spirit

1 **a)** Match the definitions from the *Longman Dictionary of Contemporary English* with the pictures and write the correct word in the spaces.

1 ...*body building*... *n* [U] an activity in which you do hard physical exercise in order to develop big muscles

2 .... *n* [C] a description of your character and the things that will happen to you, based on the position of the stars and planets at the time of your birth

3 .... *v* [I] to empty your mind of thoughts and feelings in order to relax completely or for religious purposes

4 .... *n* [C,U] a belief that some objects or actions are lucky and some are unlucky, based on old ideas of magic

5 .... *n* [C] an animal, toy, etc., that represents a team or organisation, and is thought to bring them good luck

6 .... *v* [I] to speak to God in order to ask for help or give thanks

7 .... *n* [U] the condition of not being able to sleep

8 .... *n* [U] a treatment that uses massage with pleasant-smelling oils to reduce pain and make you feel well

9 .... *n* [U] the practice or skill of treating physical problems such as back pain by moving or pressing muscles and bones

10 .... *n* [C] a meeting where people try to talk or receive messages from the spirits of dead people

b) Write sentences showing the meaning of **five** of the words above.

....

....

....

....

....

2 Write the correct word to complete each sentence.

1 The drug may make you lose your ..*appetite*... for a while.
a appetite b hunger c taste d palate
2 Bungee jumping is one of the many ....-risk sports which are becoming more and more popular nowadays.
a big b great c high d large
3 For me, there's no better way of relaxing than .... a massage after a hard day at work.
a doing b having c making d putting
4 If this diet is to work, you must .... it very strictly.
a follow b practise c pursue d go on
5 With the high altitude in Mexico City, even climbing a few stairs can leave you .... breath.
a off b needing c out of d without
6 Unfortunately, I'm allergic .... all kinds of shellfish, so I never eat prawns.
a to b at c with d about
7 Even now the illness has gone away, I still experience the occasional dizzy ....
a moment b period c spell d time
8 In an attempt to improve his physique, Manuel has decided to take up weight-............... .
a building b exercise c practice d training
9 The doctor asked me how long I'd been suffering .... insomnia.
a by b from c of d with
10 I was born on 7th July, and I met my wife in 1997 – seven is definitely my .... number!
a fortunate b glad c happy d lucky
11 Lighting is one of the many factors that can adversely .... people's mood.
a affect b effect c mark d mould
12 The illness left him extremely weak and .... to other infections.
a available b disposed c inclined d prone
13 Although I read my horoscope every day, I don't really take any .... of it.
a attention b mind c notice d part
14 I've been under so much pressure at work recently that I feel completely stressed ....
a away b off c out d over
15 Many people who are .... spiritual advice find it helpful to speak to the local priest.
a hunting b looking c searching d seeking

Grammar: adjectives and adverbs

Word order: attributive / predicative adjectives

3 Choose an adjective from the box to complete the sentences below.

~~alone~~ afraid mere alive ill live lone drunken asleep drunk sheer sick frightened only sleeping

a Since his wife died nearly twenty years ago, Walter has always lived .....*alone*...... .
b 'We were lucky to get out of there ....,' said 20-year-old Sandra Hewlett after her dramatic rescue.
c Mr Livingham denied accusations of .... behaviour at the awards ceremony. 'I only had two glasses of wine all evening,' he told journalists.
d Prices are still very low if you go to the right place: you can even get a three-course lunch for a .... €3!
e Maria felt so happy, she wanted to laugh and sing from .... joy.
f Mother Teresa spent many years working with .... children in India.
g The transportation of .... animals from one country to another remains a controversial issue.
h Her innocent expression and wide eyes gave her the look of a(n) .... animal.
i Henry gently placed his .... baby daughter into her cot.
j Who knows whether the assassination was the work of a .... gunman, or if there were others involved.
k It's often said that Antonia's .... fault was a tendency to be over-generous.
l It was 3 a.m. by the time we got home. Not surprisingly, everyone in the house was ....
m As a child, I was always .... of the dark and had to sleep with the light on.
n It was clear that many of the football supporters who started the violence had been in the bars all day and were very ....
o Tim has had to leave work early. He said he was feeling ....

Compound adjectives

4 Combine the words in brackets to form a suitable compound adjective to complete the sentences.

a The combination of loud music and flashing lights can produce a ......trance-like...... (trance like) state.

b In a ....-.......... (bad temper) second half, one player from each side was sent off by referee Ramirez.

c The ....-.......... (new appoint) head of Nookia telephones is expected to announce a new series of redundancies soon.

d After the riots, the streets of the city were filled with the wrecks of .... (burn out) cars.

e I've never tried any complementary therapies, but I think one should always be ....-.......... (open mind) about such things.

f The only jobs available are .... (bad pay) and require few qualifications.

g One of the aims of KitchenKraft is to make kitchen installations as .... (use friend) as we possibly can.

h It was only a ....-.......... (light heart) comment, and certainly not meant to give offence.

i Police are interviewing a ..........-..........-.......... (44 year old) over the disappearance of the teenager, Mandy Jones.

j Do you know who that ..........-..........-.......... (long hair) boy is? He's absolutely gorgeous, isn't he?

k The song was originally written by a ....-.......... (little know) Brazilian songwriter called Eliane Baza.

l From the airport, it's a ....-.......... (forty minute) car journey to the centre of town.

Prefixes

5 **a)** Write the opposite of the words and phrases using a word which begins with a prefix in the box below.

anti- multi- mal- mis- ~~under-~~ dis- pre- sub- un- in- over-

1 overcooked ......undercooked......
2 post-industrial ....
3 complete ....
4 understand ....
5 well-adjusted ....
6 honest ....
7 important ....
8 pro-American ....
9 monolingual ....
10 underpaid ....
11 above zero ....

b) Match each prefix in column A with **two** words in column B. Choose **five** of the words and write a definition / example sentence for them. Check your definitions / sentences in a good learner's dictionary.

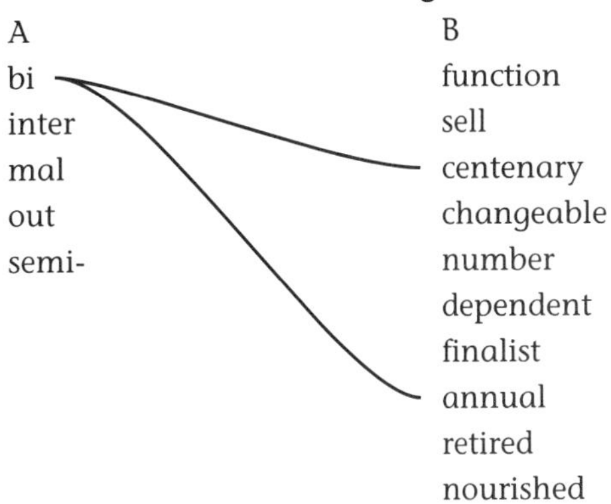

A	B
bi	function
inter	sell
mal	centenary
out	changeable
semi-	number
	dependent
	finalist
	annual
	retired
	nourished

....
....
....
....
....
....
....
....
....
....
....
....
....
....
....
....

Suffixes

6 Complete the encyclopedia entries by forming an adjective from the word in brackets. Be careful to make any necessary spelling changes (use a good learner's dictionary to help you).

neon (1) ...*colourless*.... (colour), (2) .... (odour) gas. Chemical symbol **Ne**, (3) .... (atom) number 10. Tubes containing neon are used in (4) .... (electricity) signs: it gives off a (5) .... (fire) red glow.

Neruda, Pablo (1904–1973) Chilean poet. Among his most famous (6) .... (literature) works is the epic poem *Canto General* (1950). He also served in the (7) .... (diplomacy) service and was awarded the Nobel Prize for literature in 1971.

nervous breakdown popular term for a reaction to overwhelming (8) .... (psychology) stress. There is no equivalent in (9) .... (medicine) terms. Someone suffering may become unusually (10) .... (anxiety) in (11) .... (stress) situations.

nettle stinging plants with oval, tooth-edged leaves. The (12) .... (green) leaves are slightly (13) .... (poison) and can cause a (14) .... (pain) irritation on the skin.

Newark largest city and port of New Jersey, USA. It is an important (15) .... (commerce) and (16) .... (finance) centre and the (17) .... (administration) centre of Essex county. It is also a large producer of (18) .... (electricity) equipment.

Adverbs of degree

7 Cross out the **two** adverbs of degree which cannot combine with the adjective on the right.

a ~~absolutely~~ really ~~a bit~~ quite extremely — GOOD
b very absolutely totally really slightly — FANTASTIC
c really not very completely extremely a bit — INTERESTING
d absolutely pretty quite a little utterly — PERFECT
e rather really absolutely utterly quite — TALL
f quite pretty rather 100% totally — RIGHT

Pronunciation

Stress in longer words

8 [4.1] Put each word in the box below into the correct column according to its stress pattern. Use the recording to help you.

~~allergic~~ disorderly impressive relationship alternative exercise incompetent superstition appetite horoscope interactive unconscious atmospheric imagine pregnancy unimportant

••●•	•●••	●••	•●•
			allergic

Patterns to notice

Comparative and superlative adjectives

9 Complete the text with the appropriate form of the adjective in brackets.

Summer Hazards

For city dwellers in the summer months, the (1) ....*hotter*....... (hot) it gets, the (2) .... (great) the danger from air pollution. But did you know that eating strawberries is one of (3) .... (easy) ways of resisting air pollution? They are rich in pollution-busting ellagic acid ... and what could be (4) .... (nice) than a delicious bowl of strawberries on a hot summer's day? There's nothing (5) .... (bad) than an attack of sunburn ... so no one should go out into the sun without plenty of factor 20. But the more fruit and vegetables you eat – particularly mangos, sweet potatoes, carrots and apricots – the (6) .... (resistant) your skin becomes to the sun's harmful rays. And (7) .... (good) thing about this form of sun protection is that it tastes a lot (8) .... (good) than sun cream too!
What could be (9) .... (good) for cooling off than an afternoon at the swimming pool? But be careful – the more time you spend in the water, the (10) .... (likely) it is that you'll be exposed to water-borne bacteria, which can cause ear and throat infections. If you're in and out of the swimming pool every few minutes, Xylitol, a natural sweetener from a birch tree, is among (11) .... (effective) protectors – and you can buy it in chewing-gum form – so the more you chew (12) .... (healthy) you'll be!

Listen and read

The Quest for Immortality

10 **a)** [4.2] Read and / or listen to the text below.

The Quest for Immortality

Scientific breakthroughs mean that life expectancy continues to rise every year. But the medical advances which now make it possible to contemplate living to a very great age – if not forever – also raise profound practical and ethical issues.

How long are we living now?

Over the past century, life expectancy in developed countries has risen at an astonishing rate. In Britain, for example, the average male lifespan went up from 48 in 1901 to 75 in 2000. (During the same time, the female lifespan rose from 49 to 80.) Scientists have always imagined that this rise would tail off, but that does not seem to be happening. Since 1840, people born in any year have, on average, lived three months longer than those born the previous year – a consistent increase that still holds true today. A paper published in *Science* magazine has warned that, at the current rate, female life expectancy in developed countries could be as high as 101 by 2070.

Why are we lasting so much longer?

Mainly because of better nutrition, better housing, vaccination programmes and a dramatic reduction in infant mortality due to advances in both pre-natal and post-natal care. Since there is only limited potential for further advances in these areas, some scientists think we have almost reached the limit of human longevity. Dr Jay Olshansky, of the University of Chicago, for example, believes that the only way of adding to life expectancy now is to make old people live longer – a painstaking process that will be measured in weeks or months, not years. The real challenge now facing biologists is to learn how to delay the ageing process.

So is immortality a realistic prospect?

Not for the foreseeable future. In last year's Reith lectures[1], the gerontologist Professor Tom Kirkwood firmly quashed the notion that genetic engineering might result in some kind of 'fountain of youth'. Considering how frustratingly slow the battles against cancer, heart disease and strokes have been, he said, it is fanciful to imagine that we could conquer death. On the other hand, scientists do now understand more about why we age, and what can be done to slow down the process. 'Our ancestral genes placed limited priority on long-term maintenance and repair,' says Kirkwood. 'Ageing comes about through the gradual build-up of unrepaired faults in the cells and tissues of our bodies, not as the result of some active mechanism for death and destruction.' The trick, then, is to help the body repair the damage done by wear and tear.

How can that be done?

In many different ways, some of which are already pretty commonplace. Organ transplants from pigs and monkeys are now old news – the American politician Jesse Helms has just had a ten-year-old pig valve in his heart replaced. Laser eye surgery has become so commonplace that Americans can now get it in shopping malls. Doctors have succeeded in wiring computerised implants directly to nerve fibres, allowing the deaf to hear, and there is hope that electrodes planted in the brain may soon offer hope for the blind to see. But the real potential at the moment lies in the field of stem cells – special cells that allow lizards to grow new tails and humans to grow new skin over minor cuts. If scientists can learn how to control these cells, they could be used to regenerate parts of the body that are failing.

[1] an annual series of BBC radio lectures given on a scientific topic

b) Read the statements below. Based on the information in the text, mark them P (possibly true), D (definitely true) or U (unlikely).

1 People in the UK are living much longer than they used to. .D.
2 It will be common for women to live to over 100 in the year 2070. ....
3 Infant mortality will continue to fall sharply. ....
4 Life expectancy will not carry on rising as dramatically as in the past. ....
5 One day, we may be able to live forever. ....
6 Scientists understand much more about the ageing process nowadays. ....
7 Replacing body parts is now a common operation. ....
8 There will be a cure for blindness in the future. ....

Check your pronunciation

11 a) [4.3] Listen again to this extract from the text. Pause at the points indicated and look at the *Pronunciation points* below.

1 **Why are we lasting so much longer? (1)** Mainly because of better nutrition, better housing, vaccination programmes and a dramatic reduction
5 in infant mortality (2) due to advances in both pre-natal and post-natal care. Since there is only limited potential (3) for further advances in these areas, some scientists think we have
10 almost reached the limit of human longevity (4). Dr Jay Olshanksy, of the University (5) of Chicago, for example, believes that the only way of adding to life expectancy now is to make old
15 people live longer – a painstaking process that will be measured in weeks or months, not years. The real challenge now facing biologists is to learn how to delay the ageing process.

LOOK!

Pronunciation points

1 Notice the intonation in the question *Why are we lasting so much longer?* This indicates that the speaker is especially interested or puzzled.

2 Notice the intonation of the items in the list: the voice goes up on the first (*nutrition, housing, programmes, reduction*) and down on the last item (*infant mortality*).

3 Notice the /ʃə/ sound in *potential*. It is also heard in *nutrition* (line 2), *vaccination* (line 3) and *reduction* (line 4).

4 Notice the stress pattern in the word *longevity* ●●●● . The following words have a similar stress pattern: *mortality* (line 5) and *expectancy* (line 14).

5 Notice how *the* and *University* are linked with a /j/ sound. Notice the similar way in which *the only* (line 13) and *the ageing* (line 19) are pronounced.

b) Practise reading the passage yourself, paying attention to the *Pronunciation points* above. Use the recording to help you if necessary.

Wordspot

Idioms to do with the body

12 a) Complete the sentences with the appropriate part of the body.

1 The police seem to be turning a blind ....*eye*.......... to his activities.
2 I tried not to laugh, but I couldn't keep a straight ....
3 He won the final .... down.
4 I just can't get my .... round these instructions.
5 Is that true or are you pulling my .... ?
6 Everything in her garden grows beautifully: she has green ....
7 It was a .... -raising experience: I was terrified!
8 I offered my cat some biscuits, but she turned her .... up at them.
9 Busy? I'm up to my .... in it.
10 Daniela cooked us a .... -watering meal.
11 As the big moment approached, I could feel the butterflies in my ....
12 'How's your lovely wife?' I asked David ... and remembered they'd just got a divorce. I'd put my .... in it as usual.
13 Oh no! I've dropped it. I'm all fingers and .... today.
14 It was a .... -rending speech – everyone was very moved.

b) Match the illustrations to six of the expressions above.

Check your writing

Confusing spellings

13 a) The words in the box can be confusing because of their spelling. Write the word next to the appropriate definition.

advice effect loose advise prize flair lose relief affect flare pain relieve price strait breathe breath life pane live straight

1 ....*advice*..... *n* [U] an opinion you give someone about what you should do

2 .... *v* [T] to tell someone what you think they should do

3 .... *n* [C, U] the way in which an event, action or person changes someone or something

4 ....*v* [T] to do something that produces a change in someone or something

5 .... *n* [C] the air that you take in and send out from your lungs

6 .... *v* [I, T] to take air into your lungs and send it out again

7 .... *n singular* a natural ability to do something

8 .... **up** *v* [I] (of a disease or illness) to suddenly become worse or more painful

9 .... *adj* [only before noun] 1 not dead or artificial 2 a performance that is for an audience of people rather than for a film / recording

10 .... *n* [C] the period between a person's birth and death

11 .... *adj* not firmly fixed in place or tight

12 .... *v* 1 not to win a game or argument 2 to be unable to find something that you had before

13 .... *n* [C,U] the feeling you have when a part of your body hurts

14 .... *n* [C] a sheet of glass used in a window or a door

15 .... *n* [C] the amount of money for which something is bought, offered or sold

16 .... *n* [C] something that is given to someone who has been successful in a competition, race, game, etc.

17 .... *n singular* [U] a feeling of comfort when something frightening, worrying or painful has ended or not happened

18 .... *v* [T] to make a pain, problem, unpleasant feeling less severe

19 .... *adj* something which is not curved or curly

20 .... *n often plural* [C] a narrow passage of water between two areas of land, usually connecting two seas

b) Tick (✓) the sentences in which the word in italics is spelt correctly. Correct the ones where it is spelt incorrectly.

1 Can I ask your *advice* about a personal problem? ✓ ....
2 He won first *price* in a competition. ....*prize*.......
3 Trouble began to *flair* up between police and demonstrators. ....
4 Try not to let the pressure *affect* you – just stay calm and focused. ....
5 He was wearing a *loose*-fitting shirt which looked very good on him. ....
6 The doctor has prescribed some painkillers to *relief* the pain. ....
7 I'd say he has enough to set him up for *live*. ....
8 I'm going to see the doctor about the *pane* in my chest. ....
9 We crossed a narrow *straight* of water separating the two islands. ....
10 One of the main *affects* of global warming is rising sea levels. ....
11 It was stupid of me to *loose* my temper like that. ....
12 I love the sound of raindrops on the window *pane*. ....
13 The group are to play some *life* concerts in May. ....
14 It was so hot in there it was hard to *breath*. ....
15 I felt it was a *fair* price to pay for such a beautiful item. ....
16 It was such a *relieve* that my coat hadn't been stolen. ....
17 It was so funny, I couldn't keep a *strait* face. ....
18 Would you *advice* me to go on a diet, doctor? ....
19 Running up those stairs has left me out of *breath*. ....
20 We need someone with a real *flare* for design. ....

Do you remember?

Page 36-37

1 **What is the title of the module?** ....

2 **What, according to the saying, are the windows to the soul?** ....

3 **What part of their body do people sometimes have read in order to predict the future?** ....

4 **Which of the following is not a complementary therapy?**

a aromatherapy b insomnia c osteopathy

5 **Write the adjective form of these nouns.**

a luck .... b spirit ....

c allergy ....

6 **What phrasal verb means *to discover information, or learn something*?** ....

Pages 38-39

7 **What idiom means: *to accept something new without letting it trouble you in any way*?** ....

8 **Which therapy did Alison Hatch try?** ....

9 **When the therapist asked Alison what she was stressed about, what was her answer?** ....

10 **Supply the prepositions in this sentence from the text.**

She would then talk (1).................... whatever problems had come (2).................... (3).................... the beginning of the session and she counted back (4).................... ten and took me (5).................... .

11 **What was Alison's answer to the little boy's question: *Miss, what are you doing?*** ....

12 **What are the other three therapies described?** ....

Pages 40-41

13 **Match the two halves of the compound adjectives.**

bad	up	....
laid	minded	....
open	back	....
worked	tempered	....

14 **Which of the adjectives below can complete the sentence?**

The consultation was very ....

a detailed b initial c long d thorough

15 **What does the prefix *inter-* mean?** ....

16 **Which word means: *a large number of things that are scattered somewhere in an untidy way*?** ....

17 **What kind of walk is among the most effective forms of exercise?** ....

18 **Scientists from which university have discovered that palmistry may have some basis in scientific truth?** ....

Pages 42-43

19 **What word in the *Useful language box* means: *very worried or nervous about something*?** ....

20 **What is the missing modal verb in these example sentences?**

a It .... easily have happened.

b She .... have felt terrified.

c Personally, I don't think she .... have ...

21 **What is Glynn Griffith's job?** ....

22 **How much is the top prize?** ....

23 **What phrase means: *the person or team who finishes second in a competition*?** ....

24 **What is the word for someone who has been nominated for an award?** ....

Pages 44-45

25 **If you win very easily, do you win: *feet down, fingers down, hands down or thumbs down*?** ....

26 **What do you have in your stomach when you feel very nervous?** ....

27 **What are you likely to do if you are *all fingers and thumbs*?** ....

28 **What is the name of the fitness centre?** ....

29 **Which person at the fitness centre:**

a will provide you with an exercise video? ....

b can design a diet for you? ....

30 **What is the minimum period for which you can join the fitness centre?** ....

module 5

Vocabulary

Education

1 Copy the words and phrases in the box below into the appropriate column.

~~elementary~~ professor graduation nursery lecture undergraduate online learning refresher course junior toddler skip lectures full marks grades primary drop out degree

children's education (before 15)	adult education	both
elementary		

Collocations

2 Underline the best option to complete the sentences.

a The school aims to encourage people to take a full *part* / *place* / *piece* in society.

b The new town council has promised to *cope with* / *deal with* / *treat* the problem of urban crime.

c Mazda is a company which tries to give all its employees a(n) *comment* / *opinion* / *say* in how the business is run.

d Retirement will give Henderson the chance to *chase* / *pursue* / *take after* his other interests.

e There have been a number of attempts to encourage young people to become *activated* / *concerned* / *involved* in criminal activities.

f There's no doubt that high unemployment plays a *factor* / *role* / *roll* in increasing the crime rate.

g The Conference will be an ideal opportunity for teachers and students to get together and *share* / *distribute* / *give out* their experiences.

h This match provides us with an excellent *occasion* / *opportunity* / *place* to try out some new players.

i It was Oscar Wilde who made the famous *announcement* / *observation* / *allegation* that nothing worth knowing can be taught.

j Children at primary school do not only learn the three Rs: they also begin to develop social *abilities* / *skills* / *talents* which they will need throughout their school and working life.

Word building

3 **a)** Complete the table below. Mark the main stress on each word. Use a dictionary if necessary.

verb	person	noun	adjective
1 *found*	2 ………	foundation	
3 ………	4 ………	lecture	
5 ………	graduate	6 ………	
	scientist	7 ………	8 ………
		9 ………	anxious
educate	10 ………	11 ………	12 ………
expect		13 ……… 14 ………	15 ………
speculate	16 ………	17 ………	18 ………
volunteer	19 ………		20 ………

b) Choose ten of the words and write a sentence to show the meaning.

Sir Isaac Newton is often considered to be the founder of modern science.

Patterns to notice

Particles which add meaning to verbs

4 **a)** Complete the phrases below with the correct dependent preposition.

1 aimed ...at... people in their 20s
2 call someone .... their first name
3 tell him .... your problem
4 suffer .... an aching back
5 do something .... your problem
6 thinking .... what she said
7 work .... a multinational corporation
8 to gaze .... some coloured lights
9 subjected her .... an awful experience
10 what I dislike .... my city is
11 believe .... life after death
12 shout .... someone in a rude way
13 worry .... somebody
14 pay .... a meal
15 blame someone else .... what happened

b) Write in the verbs in the correct place in the table.

about	at	by	for	from	in	to
	aim					

5 Complete the sentences with a suitable particle from the box below.

down	out (x3)	up	away	around	on	~~off~~	to

a 'Where have you been? How many times do I have to tell you not to wander ...off... without telling me?'
b It took a minute or so for the laughter to die ...., allowing Martin to resume his speech.
c Lisa is going to give .... programmes to members of the audience as they come in.
d It's Linda's responsibility to lock .... when the school closes at 9 o'clock.
e If you want to write .... us, our website address is www.mtv.co.
f Despite the torrential rain, the band played ...., and the audience clapped and cheered.
g It's time someone had the courage to speak .... and reveal who is responsible for this appalling situation.
h The bus didn't leave for another three hours, so we had nothing to do but wait .... getting bored.
i Although Donna was quite shy to begin with, after a few minutes she was chatting .... quite happily.
j Our company is sending .... sample copies to thousands of potential customers.

Pronunciation

Different pronunciations of *-ch*, *-gh*, *-th* and *-ss*

6 **a)** [5.1] Listen to the example words showing the different ways in which *-ch*, *-gh*, *-th* and *-ss* are pronounced.

1 **-ch** /tʃ/ approach children
/k/ school ache

2 **-gh** /f/ cough laugh
(silent) through sought

3 **-th** /θ/ earth throw
/ð/ together without

4 **-ss** /s/ possibility stress
/ʃ/ admission passion

b) In the words and phrases below, decide how the underlined letters are pronounced. Write the correct symbol in the space.

1 a mathematical calculation /θ/
2 a leather jacket / /
3 cheer up / /
4 a tough question / /
5 out of breath / /
6 successful / /
7 weight-training / /
8 pressured into something / /
9 use a technique / /
10 have a breather / /
11 fair enough / /
12 keep a straight face / /
13 daily assembly / /
14 a great deal of discussion / /
15 join in the chorus / /
16 the punch line / /
17 a neighbouring country / /
18 a proactive approach / /
19 neither here nor there / / / /
20 all fingers and thumbs / /
21 a scholarship / /
22 a rough draft / /
23 a big issue / /
24 recess / /

c) [5.2] Listen to the recording and check your answers.

Grammar: passive forms

Passive forms with *be*

7 Complete the text using the correct passive form.

Back from the Dead? Scientists Closer to Cloning Tasmanian Tiger

Around the world, hundreds if not thousands of species of animals (1) ..*are threatened*... (threaten) with extinction ... but the latest scientific developments could mean that one day even extinct animals (2) .... (bring back) to life using DNA technology. The last-known Tasmanian tiger died in a zoo in Hobart, Australia in 1936. Fifty years later, the species (3) .... (declare) extinct. But in 1999, a research project into DNA cloning (4) .... (set up) at the Australian Museum in Sydney, and now, after three years work, high quality DNA (5) .... (extract) from a baby tiger which (6) .... (preserve) in a jar of alcohol since 1866. According to scientists, there is now a chance of the Tasmanian tiger (7) .... (resurrect) using techniques similar to those which (8) .... (use) to create cloned sheep in the 1990s. If undamaged DNA (9) .... (recover), it could (10) .... (insert) into the empty egg of a related living species, such as a Tasmanian Devil.

However, the technology for the final stage of cloning – where the Tasmanian Tiger's DNA (11) .... (place) into a Tasmanian Devil host which (12) .... (strip) of its own genetic material – is still (13) .... (develop).

'It's a very significant breakthrough,' said Professor Michael Archer, Professor of Zoology at the University of New South Wales. 'Although there's still a lot of work (14) .... (do), there's now a real possibility of Tasmanian tigers (15) .... (released) into the wild within the next decade.'

Using passive forms with reporting verbs

8 Complete the sentences using the correct form of the words in brackets.

a The marriage between singer Frankie Martin and the actress Lorna Reed ....*was supposed to be*....... (supposed / be) the perfect match: but in fact it only lasted a year.

b The killer .... (believe / escape) in a stolen car which was later found abandoned.

c During the 1960s, this kind of furniture .... (consider / be) the last word in style and good taste.

d The former champion .... (not think / consider) a come-back at present.

e American TV star Hope de Loris .... (rumour / spend) $1.4 million on a lavish new home ... for her pet dog!

f New crime figures released by the government .... (expect / show) a dramatic rise in offences committed by young people.

g Actor Mel Donnelly insisted that his remarks .... (not intend / cause) offence, and he offered his full apologies to the audience.

h Raimondo's new sponsorship deal with Badidas .... (report / be) worth €5 million over the next six years.

i The police were taking no risks, as the man they were looking for .... (know / be) armed and dangerous.

j The Foreign Minister .... (allege / be) involved in extreme left-wing politics during his student days in the 1970s.

k Although he was admitted to hospital late on Thursday, the 82-year-old actor's medical condition .... (not understand / be) life-threatening.

l The getaway car which police have found by the side of a main road .... (assume / be) stolen the previous day.

Passive forms without *be*

9 Improve the style of the newspaper article below by crossing out 14 words which are unnecessary or incorrect.

1 **Bananas and Bach Diet ~~has been~~**
2 **Approved for Exam Pupils**

3 Pupils who have been enrolled for exams at
4 a Nottingham school will be fed a diet of
5 bananas and classical music. Teachers at
6 Kensal Green Girls' School hope their
7 students' brain power will be increased by
8 the special regime. When she was
9 interviewed on local television, head teacher
10 Sarah Weaver said, 'Every girl will be
11 given a banana on exam mornings to help
12 them get their brains into gear.' Soothing
13 classical music – which is played at low
14 volume through concealed speakers – is
15 believed to calm candidates' nerves and
16 put them in a relaxed frame of mind as they
17 enter the examination hall. The experiment –
18 which is based on similar techniques used in
19 US universities – is likely to be imitated in
20 other Nottingham schools if it is found to
21 be successful.

Passive forms with *get* and *have*

10 Complete the sentences with the correct form of *get* or *have* and the words in brackets.

a You can't go to a formal party dressed like that. You'd better .....*get changed*...... (change).
b Can't you ever drive anywhere without us .... (lost)?
c Nobody seemed to care about the abandoned car in front of the house. In the end we had to pay .... (removed).
d We had only been driving across country for a few miles when the van .... (stuck) on the muddy track.
e There's someone at the door. If I were you, I .... (dressed) and see who it is.
f Right, everybody ... it's 8.30 and I think you'd agree that it's time we .... (started).
g It took us nearly an hour, but in the end we managed .... (the piano) up the staircase.
h If you don't make some attempt to conceal your jewellery, there's a good chance that it .... (stolen).
i Ali had high hopes of winning the tennis tournament, but in fact he .... (beaten) in the very first round.
j No matter how carefully I pack my suitcase, my shirts always seem .... (creased).
k TV presenter Mary-Anne Pickford and her rock star boyfriend Dave Gavin are rumoured .... (engaged) during their romantic holiday in Greece.
l I think Michelle's at the hairdresser. She's probably .... (hair / done) right now.
m I'm sorry about the meal ... I forgot I'd put it in the oven and I think it .... (burn).
n Natalia .... (ears / pierced) when she was just a toddler.

Listen and read

From a Distance

11 **a)** [5.3] Read and / or listen to the article about distance learning.

From a Distance

A Brief History of Distance Learning

1 **distance learning** *n* [U] a method of study that involves using electronic means (computers, Internet, etc.) to receive and send work rather than going to a school or university

'Knowledge,' according to the proverb 'is power.' And in this 5 electronic age, more and more of our information is gained not in the classroom, but via media such as the Internet, CD-ROM and cable TV ... all of which are playing a key part in the distance learning revolution. Here are three figures in this key educational change which is transforming our lives in the 21st 10 century ...

Sir Isaac Pitman

Those who think that distance learning is a relatively new idea might 15 be surprised to learn that English educator, Sir Isaac Pitman, had the same idea – only then they were called correspondence 20 courses – more than 150 years ago. Taking advantage of the development of a reliable postal system in 1840, 25 Pitman began teaching shorthand[1] by mail to thousands of students who did not have time to attend school. 'Lessons' consisted of copying short passages of the Bible in shorthand, and posting them to Mr. Pitman to be corrected. His brother, Benn Pitman, 30 introduced the idea to the United States, and the Pitman shorthand system – which has been adapted to fifteen other languages – is still one of the most widely used shorthand systems in the world.

The Open University

35 When it was established in 1969, the Open University offered courses via mail, with the back-up of regular TV and radio 40 programmes shown outside normal broadcast times. Each student was assigned a tutor who discussed the course work 45 over the phone, and in group sessions in the evenings or at weekends.

Thirty years on, the Open University has expanded to include the Internet, videoconferencing, satellite broadcast and e-50 mail. There are no entry qualifications or admission interviews, and anyone over the age of 18 can follow one of their courses. It is now Britain's largest single teaching institution, with more than 200,000 people studying its courses every year, with another 16,000 in other countries 55 around the world.

John Hendricks and The Discovery Channel

After a successful career in university education, John S Hendricks entered the TV business and launched the Discovery Channel – the first cable TV channel exclusively 60 devoted to documentaries and nature programmes – in June 1985. Today the company's programmes reach over 150 million subscribers in more than a hundred countries. In an age where competition for TV audiences has never been tougher, the Discovery Channel's high-quality, educational 65 approach continues to defy those who believe that TV is only about mindless entertainment. The BBC programme *Walking with Dinosaurs* became the most-watched documentary in TV history when it was shown on the Discovery Channel in 2000.

[1] a system for writing down what people are saying using special signs to represents words, letters and phrases

b) According to the texts:

1 who first had the idea of teaching shorthand by correspondence? ...*Sir Isaac Pitman*...
2 who took the idea of correspondence courses to theUnited States? ....
3 what three methods were originally used for course work by the Open University? ....
4 what entry qualifications are required to do a course at the Open University? ....
5 what type of programmes are shown on the Discovery Channel? ....
6 what programme attracted the most viewers ever for a TV documentary? ....

Check your pronunciation

12 [5.4] Listen to the phrases below. Notice the pronunciation of the letters in bold in each case. Practise saying the phrases yourself.

a more of our informa**tion**
b dist**ance** learning
c **sh**ort passa**ges**
d group se**ssion**s
e admi**ssion** interviews
f a su**cc**e**ss**ful career
g TV audien**ces**
h mindle**ss** entertainment

Wordspot

way

13 Complete the sentences.

a It's ...on... its way.
b If something is blocking you, it's .... the way
c This is the wrong ʍɐʎ ....
d MOVE! Will you please get .... of the way!
e I want a much bigger one, This is way .... small!
f If you take extra trouble, you go .... of your way to do something.
g She's determined to have her .... way.
h If you're lost, you can always .... the way.
i ... but some people prefer to try and .... the way themselves!
j If you go first, you .... the way.
k You shouldn't get lost if you .... the way.
l This is the wrong ʏɒw ....!

Check your writing

Linking words and phrases (2)

14 Read the set of tips below. Underline the best linking word or phrase.

How to Improve your Desk Space

* Prevent back problems (1) *because of* / *by* / *if* / *when* using a height-adjustable desk (2) *it* / *what* / *which* / *whose* can be electronically raised so you have intervals of sitting down and then standing up.
* Your feet should be flat on the ground (3). *If not,* / *In case* / *So that* / *Therefore* you need to buy a footrest.
* Position the computer screen an arm's length away, adjusting the height (4) *for* / *in order for* / *so as to* / *so that* your eyes are in line with the top.
* Make sure there is sufficient light for your desk. (5) *As well* / *Consequently* / *However* / *Therefore* try not to allow light to reflect off your screen causing a glare.

* Tilt your screen slightly downwards: when your head is angled down your eyelids cover more of your eyeballs, (6) *for helping* / *helping* / *it helps* / *that helps* to keep them moist.
* Don't put reading material flat on the desk. (7) *In addition* / *Instead* / *Otherwise* / *Unless* put paper on a copy-holder or stand so you can read comfortably.
* Learn to use your mouse with both hands (8) *for* / *it can* / *in order to* / *which* prevent Repetitive Strain Injury.

Do you remember?

Pages 46-47

1 **What is the title of the module?**

....

2 **What three types of course are mentioned in C ?**

....

3 **What phrasal verb means: *to leave a course before it finishes*?** ....

4 **You will usually find professors working in secondary schools. True or False?** ....

5 **What are *the Three Rs*?** ....

6 **What does a *vocational course* prepare you for?**

....

Pages 48-49

7 **The research on the effects of television was done with 200 – who?** ....

8 **According to the saying, what does the early bird catch?** ....

9 **What word comes before the words *toys, material* and *videos*?** ....

10 **In which country was the research about children's anxieties done?** ....

11 **Complete the title of one of the texts: *We All Have Genius* .... *Us*.**

12 **What is the name of the film about an idiot savant featuring Dustin Hoffman?** ....

Pages 50-51

13 **Which particle adds the idea of pointless activity, *around* or *away*?** ....

14 **What phrasal verb means: *to go to the airport / station,* etc., *to say goodbye to someone*?**

....

15 **If someone *reads out* something, do they:**

a read it aloud? b continue reading it?
c read it silently?

16 **What is the name of the head teacher at the Phoenix High School in London?** ....

17 **What three things are mentioned as *social evils*?**

....

18 **Which of these words are spelt incorrectly?**

a expeariences b observations c opportunaty
d tolerence e perspectives

Pages 52-53

19 **Rearrange the words to make a sentence.**

are / buying CDs / Expectant / into / like / mothers / *Mozart for mothers-to-be* / pressured

....

....

20 **Choose the modal verb to complete the sentence.**

There's something important that I had to / must have / should have mentioned before.

21 **What word means the same as *extremely important*?** ....

22 **The task is to teach what to others?**

....

23 **List eight parts of the body mentioned in the instructions for giving mouth-to-mouth resuscitation.**

....

....

24 **What phrase means: *carefully, in a logical order*?**

....

Pages 54-55

25 **The writing task is to write what from notes?**

....

26 **Which is the correct form in the sentence?**

Try *type* / *to type* / *typing* a plus sign between the words.

27 **If something is blocking the path, is it *in the way* or *on the way*?** ....

28 **Which is the correct form in the sentence?**

No way *I'm going to* / *am I going to* / *I'll* do that.

29 **Is *going out of your way to help someone* a way of avoiding helping them, or giving them extra help?** ....

30 **What are the missing verbs?**

a .... the way (= discover the route somewhere)

b .... the way (= be familiar with the route somewhere)

c .... the way (= ask for directions)

module 6

Vocabulary

Double your money

1 Choose a word or phrase from the box below to complete the sentences.

broke priceless ~~tip~~ pension subsidy bribes worthless stingy fee automatic cash machine bankrupt ransom

a The waitress was so rude, and the service so slow, that we decided not to leave a ....tip........ at the end of the meal.
b I just couldn't believe my eyes when I saw the .... that my lawyer had charged me ... € 750!
c The Star of Africa – belonging to the Queen of England – is the largest cut diamond in the world and is regarded as utterly ....
d Unfortunately, many of the 'authentic' autographs bought and sold on the Internet are not genuine, and as such are completely ....
e Despite being one of the richest men in the USA, Texas oil billionaire H L Hunt was so .... he refused to buy lunch: he always brought his own sandwiches to meetings!
f Some politicians are arguing that the .... given to support the unprofitable transport system is too high.
g Now they've retired, my grandparents only have their .... to live on.
h The young man was released by the kidnappers when his family agreed to pay a .... of $100,000.
i K P Internet Services, which has been making huge losses over the last three years, finally went .... last month.
j At the time of his arrest, the former company director was homeless and completely ....
k The city mayor is at the centre of a scandal in which he is accused of accepting .... from local businessmen.
l Oh no! The .... has taken my card and the bank's closed. What can I do?

Definitions

2 **a)** Match the words in the box below to the definitions.

~~resume~~ smart backpacker ratings grasp commuter ingenious convict speechless top lavish flip

1 ....resume.... *formal* to start doing something again after a pause or interruption
2 .... *adj* clever, original and effective
3 .... *n* [C] a person who travels around on holiday carrying their possessions in a large bag on their back
4 .... *adj* large and generous, and looking as if it costs a lot of money
5 .... *n* [C] someone who travels a long distance to work every day
6 .... *adj* one of the best or most successful
7 .... *n* your ability to understand a complicated idea or situation
8 .... *adj especially AmE* clever, intelligent
9 .... *v BrE* to spin a flat object such as a coin into the air as a way of deciding something
10 .... *n* [C] someone who has been found to be guilty of a crime and sent to prison
11 .... *n pl* a list which shows which films, television programmes, etc., are the most popular
12 .... *adj* unable to speak because you feel very angry, upset, etc.

b) Choose **five** of the words. Write an example sentence to show their meaning.

....
....
....
....
....

Pronunciation

Diphthongs

3 **a)** [6.1] Diphthongs are two vowel sounds pronounced together. Listen to the examples, and practise saying the sounds and the words.

1 / eɪ / way
2 / ɔɪ / boy
3 / əʊ / go
4 / aɪ / buy
5 / aʊ / now
6 / eə / dare

b) Put the words in the box below into the correct column.

~~claim~~ broke doubt grow rate coin tight bear bribe borrow count toy fair drown join

1 / eɪ / way
claim ....
....

2 / ɔɪ / boy
....
....

3 / əʊ / go
....
....

4 / aɪ / buy
....
....

5 / aʊ / now
....
....

6 / eə / dare
....
....

c) [6.2] Listen to the recording and check your answers. Practise saying the words.

Grammar: time and tense

General

4 Read the joke about Sherlock Holmes and Dr Watson. Write **one** example of each verb form in the table below. Which verb form is **not** included?

	Simple	Continuous
Present		
Present Perfect		
Past		*were having*
Past Perfect		
Future		
Future Perfect		

Elementary, my dear Watson

1 Sherlock Holmes and Dr Watson were having a camping holiday in the countryside. On their final evening, they decided to go to bed as soon as they had
5 finished their simple meal, as they were leaving early the next morning.

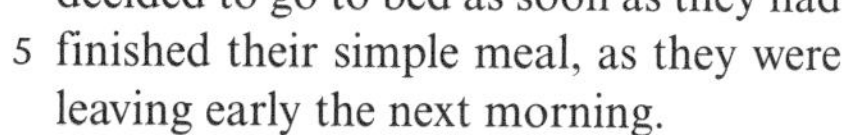

Some time later, Watson woke up. He saw his friend was lying awake, staring at the stars. He had obviously been doing this for some time.

'Watson,' said Holmes, 'I have been studying the stars for the last ten minutes
10 and I have just made a brilliant deduction. Before I tell you what it is, look up at the stars and tell me what **you** see.'

Watson thought for a moment.

'Well, the stars are shining brightly, which means it will probably be a wonderful day tomorrow.'

15 'No, not that,' said Holmes. 'Try again.'

'Let me see … I observe that the Moon is at angle of 65 degrees, and will be setting in approximately one hour. I therefore deduce that the time is approximately 2.25 a.m.'

'No, not that either,' said Holmes. 'Try again.'

20 'Um … in another five hours, we will have been on holiday for exactly one week.'

'You idiot, Watson. Some thief has stolen our tent!'

Unusual uses of 'present' verb forms

5 **a)** Complete the sentences with the correct form of the verb in brackets.

1 A hamburger ....*walks*.......... (walk) into a bar. The barman says, 'Sorry, we ......*don't serve*....... (serve) food.'
2 Don't forget to pick up all your belongings before you .... (leave).
3 In the opening chapter, Pip, the hero of the novel, ... (have) a terrifying encounter with a convict.
4 Santa Rosa man .... (deny) tax charges. (Full story page 2.)
5 The police .... (be) to introduce a new identity card scheme for teenagers.
6 So it is with great pride that I .... (declare) this supermarket open ...
7 We're determined to enjoy the game, whether or not our team .... (win).
8 And Foster .... (smash) that ball into the net ... love–40!
9 The next person who .... (shout out) will receive a punishment. Please put your hands up!
10 According to this, the next train .... (leave) till 10 o'clock. What shall we do?

b) Match each sentence to one of the uses of the Present Simple below.

- To talk about past situations in newspaper headlines. ..*4*..
- To talk about the past when we tell a joke, relate a story, book or play. ......
- To refer to an action which happens at the moment of speaking. ......
- To describe or commentate on a present action. ......
- To describe future events which are programmed or timetabled. ......
- To refer to the future after time conjunctions such as *if, when, before, as soon as,* etc. ......
- After relative pronouns such as *who* and *where* in subordinate clauses introduced by *as, than* and *whether.* ......

Verb forms used to talk about unreal situations

6 Underline the correct form of the verb to complete the sentences.

a If I *had / have / will have* a bit more time, I'd be delighted to help.
b Do you ever wish *you listened / you'd listened / you've listened* to all the advice you were given when you were younger?
c Suppose *we took / we'd taken / we've taken* a taxi to the airport ... how much do you think it would cost?
d What would your reaction be if I *was to / were to / am to* tell you that you've been chosen to appear on TV?
e Sally and I just *wanted / have wanted / are wanting* to thank you for all the support you've given us.
f Anybody would have done the same if they *are / had been / were* in my position.
g It's time you *face up / will face up / faced up* to the truth. You have to accept that she's not coming back.
h I'm not sure how to ask you this, I *am wondering / was wondering / have wondered* if you'd like to go out with me some time.
i I'd rather you *don't make / hadn't made / didn't make* rude comments about my cooking, if you don't mind.
j Imagine you *can / could / 'd been able* have a date with anyone in the world ... who would it be?
k *Has there been / Was there / Were there* anything else I can get for you, madam?
l If I *knew / know / 'd known* how ungrateful Michael would be, I would never have agreed to help him.
m I wish I *can / could / will be able* understand what he's singing about, but I don't know a word of Spanish.
n I'd sooner we *leave / left / 'd left* as quickly as possible, if you don't mind.
o You really should have been more careful! Suppose someone *is driving / was driving / had been coming* the other way.

Tense and time: the sequence of tenses

7 Match the half-sentences and write ten correct sentences.

a Kay told me ... 7
b Kay tells me ...
c Whenever I see him ...
d When I saw him ...
e I just happened to be passing, ...
f If I happen to be passing, ...
g Whenever I happen to be passing, ...
h People hundreds of years ago believed ...
i A few people still believe ...
j Scientists proved many years ago ...

1 I can't help laughing.
2 I drop by and see her.
3 I'll drop by and see you.
4 so I thought I'd drop by and see you.
5 that the earth isn't flat.
6 the earth was flat.
7 you were having a barbecue this evening.
8 you're having a barbecue this evening.
9 I couldn't help laughing.
10 the earth is flat.

Kay told me you were having a barbecue this evening.

Patterns to notice

Inversion with negative adverbials

8 Correct the sentences below, paying attention to the negative adverbials.

a Under no circumstances ~~people should approach the criminal~~ as he is highly dangerous.
Under no circumstances should people approach the criminal as he is highly dangerous.

b Only then I noticed that something was missing.

c Rarely I have witnessed such enthusiasm.

d No way we're going to get this finished tonight.

e Seldom the economic outlook has looked so gloomy.

f Not only you lied to me, you also stole my money.

g No longer women expect men to provide for them economically.

h Not once he said 'thank you' for all the help I gave him.

i Only now I realise how foolish I was.

j Never before so many people have participated in a TV game show.

k On no account what I've told you should be revealed to anyone else.

Listen and read

Super-rich Stop Spoiling their Kids

9 **a)** [6.3] Read and / or listen to the text *Super-rich Stop Spoiling their Kids*. What exactly is *affluenza*?

Super-rich Stop Spoiling their Kids

Millionaires cut back inheritances to combat 'affluenza'

1 Pity America's rich kids. Their millionaire parents are giving away their inheritances and limiting their legacies to 'middle-class levels'. A study by Harvard University fundraiser and author, Charles W Collier, has found that as many as 600,000 5 of the 3.2 million millionaires in the US will give away the bulk of their personal fortunes for fear of spoiling their children. It is part of a growing trend in the US: the fight against 'affluenza', the problems associated with having too much money.

10 Of course, affluenza is not restricted to the US – rich people are everywhere. But it is only in the US, particularly in Los Angeles, that they have managed to elevate the matter to one of enormous public concern, with a mass of TV documentaries, magazines and even bank seminars 15 examining this trendiest of dysfunctional behaviours. Endemic as affluenza may well be, it is nothing compared with the behaviour of the super-wealthy as they take precautions against the condition affecting their offspring. This is especially so in Hollywood.

20 Take film stars Michael Douglas and Catherine Zeta-Jones, for example. Among their son Dylan's christening gifts was a charity foundation, worth an estimated $1.65m, established to teach the boy how to give away money. 'We shall see how he deals with this duty before giving him any more,' the 25 London *Sunday Times* quoted Douglas as saying. Said actress Jamie Lee Curtis, who together with film director husband Christopher Guest has adopted two children, Annie and Thomas: 'I want them to have enough money to pay a restaurant bill, not buy the restaurant and fire the waiter.'

Michael Douglas and Catherine Zeta-Jones

Christopher Guest and Jamie Lee Curtis

30 Susan Sarandon, who has two sons, Jack and Miles, with fellow actor Tim Robbins, put it this way: 'Money addles the brain. I see enough damaged Hollywood brats around us to see what happens when parents are content to show their love posthumously.' The rich don't want their children to end up 35 like Raphael de Rothschild, heir to one of the world's largest fortunes. He was found dead, at 23, on a New York pavement two years ago after overdosing on heroin. De Rothschild was 'old money' but many among the self-made millionaires believe there is a valuable lesson to be learnt from his demise.

40 Sociologists have been quick to point out that the new rich were entrepreneurs who derived satisfaction from earning money, not spending it. One, Jeremy Brigthon, from South California University, points out that many of them were brought up in the 1960s with 'liberal guilt' about money. 45 'That is why Bill Gates, the richest man in the world, said he would not leave his family more than $100-million,' Brigthon said. 'He and his wife, Melinda, do not want their two children to live a paranoid, pointless life. This is true of an increasing number of newly wealthy people beyond New 50 York and Washington.'

Melinda and Bill Gates

One particular fact that has alarmed the nouveau riche has found its way onto affluenza-related websites, and that is: the world's dollar billionaires together possess almost as much wealth as the poorest 50% of the planet's population; that is, 55 just 358 people have as much money as about 2.5 billion others.

b) According to the information in the text, write the name of the person or people who:

1 is critical of other Hollywood parents and their spoiled children? ...*Susan Sarandon*.....
2 want to ensure their two children have a clear purpose in life? ....
3 conducted research into what US millionaires plan to do with their money after they die? ....
4 died at a very young age from drug abuse despite being the heir to a huge fortune? ....
5 set up a special charitable organisation for their son to contribute to? ....
6 wants her children to have enough money to enjoy themselves, but not enough to abuse it? ....
7 is critical of Hollywood parents who think it's enough to leave their children money in their will? ....
8 suggests a link between the fight against affluenza and the era people grew up in? ....

Check your pronunciation

10 a) [6.4] Listen again to this extract from texts. Pause at the points indicated and look at the *Pronunciation points* below.

1 Pity America's rich kids. Their millionaire parents (1) are giving away their inheritances and limiting their legacies to 'middle-class
5 levels'(2). A study by Harvard University fundraiser and author (3), Charles W Collier, has found that as many as 600,000 of the 3.2 million (4) millionaires in the US
10 will give away the bulk of their personal fortunes for fear of (5) spoiling their children. It is part of a growing trend in the US: the fight against 'affluenza', the problems
15 associated with having too much money.

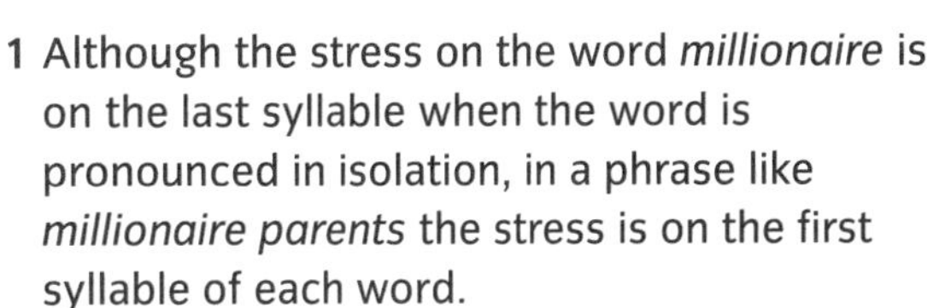

Pronunciation points

LOOK!

1 Although the stress on the word *millionaire* is on the last syllable when the word is pronounced in isolation, in a phrase like *millionaire parents* the stress is on the first syllable of each word.
2 When a phrase is printed between inverted commas (in this case because you are quoting someone else's exact words) notice that there is a short pause before and after the phrase. The same is true with 'affluenza' in line 14.
3 Notice the /ɔː/ sound in author. The same sound is found in *fortunes* in line 11.
4 The . here is pronounced as *point*: *three **point** two*.
5 Notice the pronunciation of the phrase *for fear of*: the first 'r' is silent (because it is followed by a consonant) and the second is pronounced (because it is followed by a vowel).

b) Practise reading the passage yourself, paying attention to the *Pronunciation points* above. Use the recording to help you if necessary.

Check your writing

Punctuation, symbols and abbreviations used with statistics

LOOK!

1 Full stop / point (.)

With fractions, a full stop is used to separate the numbers. It is pronounced as *point*:

4.5 = *four* ***point*** *five*

99.9 = *ninety-nine* ***point*** *nine*

It is also used for sub-headings and sub-divisions:

Figures 1.1 and 1.2

Figures one ***point*** *one and one* ***point*** *two*

2 Commas

Commas are used to separate millions, hundreds and thousands:

6,500,000

3 Hyphens (-)

Hyphens are used:

in compound adjectives

a ***four-year*** *period*

non-essential *items*

4 Brackets ( )

We use brackets when we show an equivalent amount:

900 km (600 miles)

5 Symbols

Remember that symbols for currencies are generally written **before** the number:

£50 ***US $26,000*** ***€8.50*** ***$10.50***

However, when sub-divisions of a currency are written in isolation, the symbol is written ***after*** the number:

80p ***50c*** ***60%***

6 Common abbreviations used with statistics

approx = approximately	K = thousand
bn = billion[1]	m = million
°C / °F = degrees Celsius / Fahrenheit	km^2 / m^2 = square kilometres / miles
cm = centimetres	p.a. = per annum
est. = estimated	pop. = population

[1]The American billion (one thousand million) is now more commonly used than the British billion (one million million).

11 Rewrite underlined parts of the text about Western Australia using appropriate punctuation, abbreviations, etc.

Welcome to Western Australia:

The Wildflower State

General

With an area of more than (1) 2 million 500 thousand square kilometres, Western Australia is the country's largest state and is Australia's face on the Indian Ocean. The majority of people live in and around the capital city of Perth (2) estimated population 1 million 195 thousand. Perth's new international airport handles (3) long distance flights from Africa, Asia, Europe and North America.

Climate

The state averages eight hours of sunshine per day – average monthly temperatures vary from (4) 17 degrees Centigrade approximately 62 point five degrees Fahrenheit in July to (5) 30 degrees Centigrade 86 degrees Fahrenheit in February. Most of the (6) Zero point 8 centimetres annual rainfall occurs in the winter months.

Economy and Tourism

Agriculture is Western Australia's major industry: agricultural exports earned almost (7) 2 point 9 billion dollars in 1993 to 1994. Tourism is expanding: in 1993 to 1994, more than (8) 400 thousand overseas visitors and about 5 million domestic tourists were estimated to have spent (9) 2 point 1 billion dollars on accommodation, food and pleasure shopping.

1 2,500,000 km^2
2 ....
3 ....
4 ....
5 ....
6 ....
7 ....
8 ....
9 ....

Do you remember?

Pages 56-57

1 **Complete the title of the module: .... *the Money*.**

2 **Which of these means: *without money*?**
a broke b broken c stingy d tight-fisted

3 **What's the opposite of *in the red*? ....**

4 **What is the name for the money demanded by kidnappers? ....**

5 **According to the saying, money *is the root of all* ....**

6 **Rearrange the words to make a well-known saying.**
care of / will / the pounds / and / themselves / the pennies / take / look after
....

Pages 58-59

7 **When did *Who Wants to be a Millionaire?* first appear on British TV? ....**

8 **What words follows these adjectives in the text?**
a temporary ....
b would-be ....
c highlighted ....

9 **Choose the correct forms to complete the sentence.**
The show *has sold* / *has been sold* / *is sold* to more than forty countries worldwide – in fact it's probably *been shown* / *being shown* / *shown* somewhere in the world as you read this.

10 **Paddy Spooner described himself as a *professional* ....**

11 **A *rookie* is:**
a a bird b a cheat c a newcomer

12 **On which version of *Who Wants To Be a Millionaire*? did Paddy Spooner win the least money? ....**

Pages 60-61

13 **Put the verbs into the same tense as they appear in the text.**
Everything (1).................... (go) fine, he (2).................... (say) later, until he .... (3).................... (realise) he (4).................... (forgot) to put on his mask.

14 **What did the two British robbers forget to do?** ....

15 **Choose the correct form in this sentence.**
He'll have to leave the country as soon as his visa *expired* / *has expired* / *will expire*.

16 **Where does Stella Liebeck come from?**
a Germany b Mexico c the USA

17 **What is the missing word in this sentence?**
Not once .... she admit to the crime.

18 **Choose the correct prepositions in these phrases.**
a *on* / *under* / *with* no circumstances should you ...
b *in* / *on* / *under* no account should you ...

Pages 62-63

19 **Which word completes the sentence correctly?**
He should be .... to a large sum of money.
a entitled b owed c right d titled

20 **Which word means: *everyone agreed with the decision*? ....**

21 **The smoker claims he was tricked into thinking that cigarettes were ....**

22 **What was the woman working as when she met the Texan oil tycoon? ....**

23 **What adjective goes with these nouns?**
a .... Texas oil tycoon
b .... agreement
c .... beneficiary

24 **Which word describes the father who has died?**
a ex-father b former father c late father

Pages 64-65

25 **The title of the exercise is *Writing about* ....**

26 **Choose the correct prepositions in this sentence.**
Overall, there has been an increase *in* / *of* / *on* expenditure *in* / *on* / *of* entertainment.

27 **Rearrange the letters the second word in a) – c).**
a increase glithsly ....
b drop pralshy ....
c fall etisadly ....

28 **Write in the letters to make three words meaning *very large*.**
a h_ _ _ b e_ _ _ _ _ _ _ c v_ _ _

29 **What word is used to describe a small quantity of salt? ....**

30 **Which of these combinations is not correct?**
a great deal of *money* / *people* / *time*

module 7

Vocabulary

Living together

1 Choose a word or phrase from the box below to complete the sentences.

fussy keep themselves to themselves laid back privacy grumpy sulk neat ~~irritable~~ chatty likes company unpredictable dynamic

a Kay seems unusually ....*irritable*.... today – everything seems to upset her!
b A .... person is very friendly and keen to talk.
c When we moved into the area, it wasn't easy to get to know our neighbours: people tend to ....
d Children often .... because they are angry or resentful about something.
e A .... person likes to keep things tidy.
f A .... person is always relaxed and doesn't seem to worry about things.
g Even though my great-grandmother is in her nineties, she still .... and always enjoys having visitors.
h Sunny yesterday, stormy today – the weather seems to become more .... every year – who knows what it'll be like tomorrow!
i A .... person is bad-tempered and complains a lot.
j One of the problems of sharing a flat with five other people is the inevitable lack of ....
k We need a .... person who can really motivate others to work harder.
l A .... person is too concerned about small, unimportant details.

Word building

2 Complete the sentences below by changing the word in capitals to the correct form. If necessary, use a good monolingual dictionary (e.g. *The Longman Dictionary of Contemporary English*) to help you.

a Tim shows considerable promise as an actor, despite a ....*tendency*.......... to say his lines too quickly. **TEND**
b Whatever game he's playing, Gary just hates to lose: he has an intensely .... attitude. **COMPETE**
c Despite his huge success as a musician, Jeremy was never able to earn his parents' .... **APPROVE**
d Fortunately, my friends were very .... when I made the decision to leave my job. **SUPPORT**
e Previous plans to introduce a parking scheme in the town centre have all ended in .... **FAIL**
f Nicholas has never shown the degree of .... needed to become a professional sportsman. **COMMIT**
g I think it would be much more .... to choose a 'Pay as You Go' scheme rather than pay monthly bills for your mobile phone. **ECONOMY**
h It is believed that the .... of the disease could be halted by a vaccination programme. **TRANSMIT**
i We've decided to look for a hotel in a more .... part of town. **DESIRE**
j It is completely beyond my .... why anyone would want to pull down that lovely old statue. **COMPREHEND**

Patterns to notice

Describing typical habits

3 Rewrite the sentences using the prompt and the word in brackets.

a A good friend is someone who:
- always stands by you in a crisis. (will)
  will always stand by you in a crisis.
- continues to phone you even when there's no real news. (keep)
  ....

b A bore is someone who:
- frequently talks about their boring hobbies! (always)
  ....
- often doesn't notice when other people aren't interested. (tend)
  ....

c When I was eleven, my best friend and I:
- usually walked home from school together. (used)
  ....
- always took my side if there was an argument. (would)
  ....

d My least favourite teacher at school:
- often criticised me in front of the other students. (always)
  ....
- often treated the girls better than the boys. (tend)
  ....
- repeatedly lost his temper with the students. (kept)
  ....

Grammar: infinitives and *-ing* forms

General

4 On special occasions, people often make toasts beginning *Here's to ...* . Complete the toasts below with a suitable gerund / present participle or infinitive form.

Here's to ...

a **an old friend** – someone who remembers all the secrets of our youth, but is discreet enough *not to mention* (mention) them.

b **babies** – they make our days shorter, nights longer, the past forgotten and the future worth .... (live) for.

c **happiness** – the only thing which is increased by .... (share).

d **my husband** – who buys football tickets six months in advance, but waits until Christmas Eve .... (buy) Christmas presents.

e **my darling wife** – since I met you, I have known what it is to love someone, and what it means for that love .... (return).

f **my parents** – for .... (spoil) me ever since I was a little baby. Please feel free to continue.

g **our second marriage** – we are so fortunate .... (give) a second chance at happiness.

h **success** – it takes time .... (be) a success, but time is all it takes.

i **true love** – which we find not .... (look for) a perfect person, but .... (find) an imperfect person and .... (not / see) their faults.

j **your retirement** – and while you're sitting at home with nothing to do, think of us all at work – we're sure .... (do) the same.

Infinitives and gerunds after adjectives

5 Complete the sentences with a preposition (if necessary) and the correct form of the verb in brackets.

a When I was young, my mother always made me say sorry ....*for pulling*......... (pull) my sister's hair.
b Don't be afraid .... (call) us if there's anything else you need ... that's what we're here for.
c As a politician, James is very good .... (avoid) questions which are potentially embarrassing.
d We're only here for a few days, so naturally we're keen .... (visit) as many historic sites as we can.
e If you're travelling to India, it's probably not worth .... (pack) anything warmer than a T-shirt.
f It's been a terrible experience for Andrew. Naturally he's anxious .... (return) home as soon as possible.
g The results of your test have finally arrived ... and I'm sorry .... (tell) you that the news isn't good.
h I'd never felt anxious .... (fly) until the day when we were caught in an electrical storm.
i When I looked into the office, Jill was busy .... (write) her report.
j Until quite recently, it was quite difficult for people from the West .... (visit) China.
k Because the phone line was so bad, it was very difficult .... (make out) what Florence was saying.
l It's very good .... (see) your grandmother looking so well.
m Ever since I forgot my lines in a school play, I've been afraid .... (speak) in public.
n For anyone who is keen .... (ride), there are organised pony trips every afternoon.
o I'll be very interested .... (see) what the critics say about his latest film.
p I don't understand why you won't wear a hat. Aren't you worried .... (get) cold?
q At the age of 17, I became interested .... (learn) how to cook Chinese food.
r It's still very windy, and the weather is unlikely .... (change) for the next few days.

Noun + *-ing* or infinitive forms

6 Match the half-sentences and write four grammatically correct sentences below each box.

a Herbert is in prison, but he doesn't like life in jail.

He likes the idea ... In fact, he's already made several attempts ... He and his cellmates often have arguments ... He'd probably have difficulty ...	about escaping. escaping. of escaping. to escape.

1 *He likes the idea of escaping.*.......................................
2 ....
3 ....
4 ....

b Mayor Bloodstone would like to introduce a new traffic scheme in Kenton. However, not everyone agrees with his plans.

He has plans ... He is likely to have trouble ... Not everyone sees the advantages ... Many members of the public have doubts ...	of introducing a new traffic scheme. about introducing a new traffic scheme. to introduce a new traffic scheme. introducing a new traffic scheme.

1 ....
2 ....
3 ....
4 ....

c Ali has decided to continue his studies abroad.

Ali's parents are convinced of the importance ... His parents are giving Ali the opportunity ... Ali's having a few problems ... Ali has to make some difficult decisions ...	about finding the right place to study. finding the right place to study. of studying abroad. to study abroad.

1 ....
2 ....
3 ....
4 ....

Verbs with infinitives and -*ing* forms

7 In the sentences below, only **three** of the verbs are grammatically possible. Cross out the two verbs that are incorrect.

1 It was my father who .... me to ride a motorbike.
a allowed ~~b attempted~~ c encouraged
d persuaded ~~e prevented~~

2 She .... me for causing the accident.
a accused b blamed c condemned
d criticised e suspected

3 Did they .... you go upstairs?
a ask b see c let d make e permit

4 Did you .... Frank to make that phone call?
a advise b ask c hear d remember
e remind

5 We .... travel by bus.
a daren't b had better c need d regretted
e would rather

6 The authorities .... people from travelling abroad.
a criticised b discouraged c forbid
d prevented e stopped

7 We can't .... everyone to take part.
a force b invite c let d make e tell

8 James .... talking to her.
a has forgiven me b has stopped c prevented
d remembers e saw me

9 He .... to be left alone.
a asked b begged c ordered d persuaded
e would like

10 He .... for taking the money.
a apologises b regrets c thanked her
d criticised her e admits

11 We .... them unloading the van.
a asked b heard c saw d thanked e watched

12 The police are .... people to stay at home.
a advising b not letting c making d urging
e warning

13 Robbie is being .... for causing trouble again.
a accused b blamed c criticised d prevented
e punished

14 I .... to ask my parents for more money.
a daren't b had better c need d told him
e would like

15 Who .... you to drive?
a asked b let c stopped d taught e told

Other uses of gerunds

8 Complete the gaps using the gerund or infinitive.

House Husbands' Heart Risk

Most people assume that life in the rat race is bad for your health. But (1) ....*reversing*.... (reverse) the traditional gender roles is a stressful business, according to the latest research by American scientists. By (2) .... (give) up their jobs in order (3) .... (become) house husbands, men increase their risk of heart attacks or coronary disease by as much as 82%, according to research based on a 10-year study of 2,500 people in Boston, USA.

According to Dr Elaine Eaker, the key to the problem is that some men became stressed about (4) .... (perform) a role not traditionally assigned to them by society. Men who stay at home tend (5) .... (not / have) the same levels of support from friends and family as women who do the same.

Jack O'Sullivan, of the Father's Direct group, was quoted as saying: 'Society expects the main carer (6) .... (be) a woman, and society is structured around that. Daycare is called *mother and toddler groups* and some men feel awkward about (7) .... (belong) to those groups.'

Professor Gary Cooper, a psychologist at the University of Manchester, said many men tend (8) .... (underestimate) the task of (9) .... (care) for a family. He said 'Most men think (10) .... (be) a house husband involves (11) .... (put on) a bit of washing, (12) ....(take) the kids to school and then (13) ....(put) their feet up with a cup of coffee.

They are crazy. Most men are not used to (14) .... (perform) a variety of activities simultaneously – the kind of multi-tasking which is second nature to most women.'

It is estimated that men have taken over the main homemaker's role in one in seven homes, as increasing numbers of women become the main breadwinner. The study also found that women in high-powered jobs were more likely (15) .... (develop) heart disease than those in more junior positions.

Participle clauses

9 In the news article below, some words are unnecessary. Improve the article by crossing out 13 unnecessary words. The first two have been done for you.

1 When a security van ~~which was~~ taking a group of
2 prisoners to jail in Bedford was involved in a
3 motorway pile-up, some of the convicts tried to
4 escape – but not Dennis Thynne. When the
5 23-year-old, who is currently serving a 4-year
6 sentence for burglary, saw victims of the crash
7 who were lying on the road, he leaped out of the
8 van and guided several of them to safety. 'I just
9 remember a young man who was helping move
10 injured people away from the crash,' said one
11 victim. 'I had no idea he was a convict.' The trial
12 judge, as he was hearing of Thynne's bravery, called
13 him back to court and reduced his sentence by
14 six months.

Pronunciation

Linking words

10 a) [7.1] Listen to the pronunciation of the words below, first in isolation, then in a phrase. Notice how an extra sound is used to link the two words.

1 **to** — we went out to eat /w/
2 **fear** — a fear of failure /r/
3 **be** — to be an au pair /j/

b) [7.2] Listen to the phrases. Write the appropriate symbol in the space.

1 **go** — **go and** live on a remote island /w/
2 **he** — **he always** has the radio on / /
3 **more** — I'm **more independent** nowadays / /
4 **no** — for **no apparent** reason / /
5 **so** — I was **so annoyed** / /
6 **the** — **the average** woman / /

c) Practise saying the words and phrases, copying the voices on the recording.

Patterns to notice

a lack of ..., a tendency to ..., etc.

11 Complete the sentences with a word from the box below.

~~desire~~ lack need (x2) love sense (x2) tendency fear achievement ambition total

a The Australian player's burning ....desire.... to win in front of his home crowd will make him an exceptionally difficult opponent.
b The complete .... of progress in the peace talks has led to a deep .... of frustration on both sides.
c Finally completing my university degree after so long gave me an enormous sense of ....
d Like many neglected children, Janie had a .... for approval from adults.
e The fact that Jackson was never promoted was due as much to his own lack of .... as anything else.
f In order to succeed, we must first overcome our .... of failure.
g One of the things that makes Philip so hard to work with is his .... to be in total control, which leads to a .... to be over-critical of others.
h Thomas soon got bored in the country: his .... of adventure found no expression in the daily routine of life on the farm.
i We must attribute the fact that he didn't score a single point to his .... lack of self-confidence.
j Some of the prisoners feel an enormous .... of shame about the crimes they committed.

Listen and read

Daggers Drawn

12 **a)** [7.3] Read and / or listen to the text written by Sally Magnusson, a journalist and broadcaster who lives with her family in Scotland.

Daggers Drawn

1 My daughter was singing as she polished the furniture. I hadn't asked her to polish the furniture. I never do. But where one brother is happiest with 5 the computer, one with a football and one with a model car, her idea of bliss is a can of Spring Fresh and a duster. Where have I gone wrong?

While the boys have to be nagged, 10 bribed or tricked into doing their infinitesimal share of the household chores, and can't be seen when they think they're finished, she's up on a chair with the washing-up liquid before 15 you can say 'dishes', scrubbing at pans as if her life depended on it.

Being a bit of a tomboy myself, and not too hot on the domestic skills, I used to argue till I was blue in the face 20 that the differences between men and women were all about upbringing and expectations. Nobody could have approached motherhood with a grittier determination that all children would 25 be treated the same, not channelled along some pre-ordained path. Boys would be offered soft toys to cuddle, girls would play with cars and trains. I would breed the New Men and female 30 engineers of the future.

I dare say there are indeed small boys and girls who do such things, but not mine. The hubris awaiting me was a family in which every politically 35 incorrect stereotype in the book is rife.

Ten years ago, as I gazed at my first-born in his cradle, I fantasised about the gentle soul he would be. No guns or nasty aggression for this little 40 peachblossom. He would be taught to turn away wrath with a swift word. He would grow up to be Secretary General of the United Nations.

The fantasy sustained me until he 45 was about two, when he proudly presented me with his first model – a rifle. Later on, at playgroup, he and his pals daily assassinated each other. In the garden he and his brother began 50 doing such heart-stopping things with sticks that in the end I bought them a couple of plastic swords.

We went downhill fast. A decade and three more sons after those early 55 children, we now house an arsenal of swords, rifles, water pistols, bows and arrows, hatchets, daggers and tanks that would be the envy of the British Army. Not so long ago, we were all 60 nearly arrested when a most life-like revolver in our luggage caused a security scare at Heathrow Airport.

And what of my daughter, the lone sandwiched sister? She plays all the

65 boys' games because she has to. You'll find her from time to time teetering around the house in plastic high heels, with a handbag (pink) in one hand and a shotgun in the other, and she can 70 manage a tolerable dribble down the left wing when they need someone to make up the numbers for football. But her heart is not really in it. She would much rather be drawing or writing or 75 cutting out stars or polishing shells or – dear heavens – cleaning the bathroom while waves of boys surge and roar around her.

I finally faced up to the fact that boys 80 and girls are simply born different on the day, a few years ago, when I was hanging out the washing and gave her and the next brother up a couple of clothes pegs to play with. He shot me 85 with his. She cradled it in her arms and sang it a lullaby.

But I won't give up. I'll continue to try and treat them equally and expect the same of them. And by the time 90 they're all in their teens, I imagine they'll all be equally impossible to get to do anything. But right now nature is wearing down nurture. Equality is hard work.

b) Tick (✓) the statements about the Magnusson family which are true, and put a cross (✗) by the false ones.

1 Sally Magnusson has six children – five boys and one girl. ✓
2 The boys are happy to do their share of the domestic chores. ✗
3 Her daughter likes doing the washing-up.
4 Sally likes doing the housework.
5 Sally started out determined to bring up all her children in the same way.
6 She has never allowed her sons to have toy weapons.
7 The little girl is very keen to join in with her brothers' games.
8 Sally thinks that there will be fewer problems when her children are in their teens.

Check your pronunciation

13 a) [7.4] Listen again to this extract from the text. Pause at the points indicated and look at the *Pronunciation points* below

1 And what of my daughter (1), the lone sandwiched sister? She plays all the boys' games because she has (2) to. You'll find her from time to time (3) teetering around the house in plastic high heels, with a handbag (pink) in one hand
5 and a shotgun in the other (4), and she can manage a tolerable dribble down the left wing when they need someone to make up the numbers for football. But her heart (5) is not really in it.

Pronunciation points LOOK!

1 Notice the /ɔː/ sound in *daughter*. It is also found in *all* (line 2).
2 Notice the stress on *all* and *has to* here.
3 Notice the 'weak' pronunciation of *from* and *to* in this phrase.
4 Notice how the voice goes up after *one hand* (to indicate that there is more to come) and down after *the other* (to indicate the end of that particular phrase).
5 Notice the long /ɑː/ sound in *heart*.

b) Practise reading the passage yourself, paying attention to the *Pronunciation points* above.

Check your writing

Linking words and phrases (3)

14 Choose an appropriate linker from each box to complete the texts.

while Even though This means that
In addition to On the other hand ~~also~~

All work and no play not only makes you a dull person: it (1) ....*also*.......... increases the risk of heart disease, according to the latest scientific study. It claims that people who work 60 hours a week are at high risk from heart attack, (2) .... those working a 40-hour week are much less prone to coronary disease. (3) .... this, lack of sleep brought on by overwork can triple the risk. (4) .... Britons – who work the longest hours in Europe – are at particular risk. '(5) .... people may suffer financially,' says health expert Dr Donald Minshall, 'they have to consider taking time off for the good of their health.' (6) ...., employers may be less enthusiastic about this!

Although This is because As well as that
Other than that This explains why Even if

When did someone last inspect your passport or ID card? (7) .... the majority of people in jobs in passport control are done by men, that could change. 'It's tradition, pure and simple,' according to Josef Begun.
'(8) .... there's absolutely no reason why men should be doing these jobs.'
(9) ...., when it comes to recognising faces, women beat men hands down.
(10) .... factors like hairstyle are changed, the women do better. Why? 'Most women have a role as child carer, which involves watching their children's expression very carefully.
(11) .... they seem to be better at spotting people's moods just by looking at them.
(12) ...., they seem to be more interested in the way other people look generally.'

Wordspot

just

15 Write the meaning of the word *just* in the sentences below.

only really (for emphasis) exactly
in a moment a short time ago

a 'Is the air-conditioning on too high for you?'
'No, it's just right, thank you.' ....*exactly*...........
b I'll just go and see what's happening. I won't be long. ....
c I'm sorry, but this just isn't good enough. You'll have to do it again. ....
d Let's take shelter under this tree till the rain stops ... I'm sure it's just a shower. ....
e They were just sixteen when they got engaged. ....
f You've just missed him. He'll be back later this afternoon. ....
g That's just what I was going to say! ....
h I'm just fed up with your constant moaning! Cheer up, will you? ....
i We've got just enough time to get to the station ... if you hurry up! ....
j It just takes a little patience, that's all. ....

Do you remember?

Pages 66-67

1 **Which word does not express a positive idea?**
a chatty b fussy c lively

2 **Someone who does not worry about anything can be described as .... *back*.**
a lead b laid c layed d lying

3 **Which four-word phrase means the same as *everywhere*? ....**

4 **Supply the prepositions in these phrases.**
a He keeps himself .... himself.
b Her moods change .... no apparent reason.
c He won't say what's .... his mind.

5 **Put this sentence into the past.**
One minute he's down and depressed, the next minute he'll be laughing and telling jokes.
....
....

6 **Which alternative is incorrect?**
He *keeps losing / tends losing / tends to lose* matches he ought to win.

Pages 68-69

7 **Which words should be in the *-ing* form?**
I hate people interrupt all the time and not listen properly to what others are say, it's really infuriate!
....

8 **If you avoid talking about something awkward, you are *beating about the* ....**

9 **According to Sula, watching her colleagues creep round the boss is *pretty* ....**

10 **Supply the correct forms of *to be* in this extract.**
I really hate (1) .... told what to do! I'd hate (2) .... forced to go into the army, with all that discipline, it (3) .... my personal nightmare.

11 **What was the name and nationality of the girl who was sent to a boarding school at the age of 11? ....**

12 **Which of these words are spelt incorrectly?**
a appreciate b consciencious c daunting
d inexperienced e independant

Pages 70-71

13 **What is the title of the TV show featuring six volunteers on a remote desert island?**
....

14 **In which sea is the island? ....**

15 **What is described by the following adjectives?**
a remote .... b basic ....
c primitive ....

16 **A ....*-pecked* husband is always being told what to do by his wife.**

17 **Which of these means: *I don't know*?**
I haven't got *an answer / a clue / an idea.*

18 **Is a *loner* a person who is unmarried, a person who has no brothers or sisters, or a person who prefers to be alone? ....**

Pages 72-73

19 **What idiomatic phrase describes a person who is not upset by criticism? ....**

20 **According to the text, how many words does the average woman use a day? ....**

21 **Getting men to commit themselves is like getting hold of what? ....**

22 **On what do women spend four or five times longer than men? ....**

23 **What three things are listed after *a need for*?**
....

24 **Choose the correct way to complete this sentence**
A tendency *for forgetting / of forgetting / to forget* things.

Pages 74-75

25 **Which adjective is used to describe a majority?**
a big b grand c vast

26 **What two adjectives are used to describe a minority? ....**

27 **Which phrases have the same meaning?**
a apart from that b as well as that
c because of that d other than that

28 **Supply the missing prepositions.**
a Sorry .... the mess – I'm very untidy.
b I saw Carrie .... the corridor just now.
c The woman smiled .... her son.

29 **What's the best place for *just* in this sentence?**
He phoned after you left.

30 **If tells you have *just enough money to pay*, do you:**
a have more than you need to pay?
b have the right money and no more?
c not have enough money?

module 8

Vocabulary

What's your style?

1 a) Use the clues to complete the puzzle. The number of letters for each word is given in brackets.

1 with a lot of decoration, especially with many complicated details (6, *adjective*)
2 with small holes in it to let you wear jewellery (7, *adjective*)
3 the line of hair above your eye (7, *noun*)
4 to change the colour of your clothes, hair, etc. using a liquid or powder (3, *verb*)
5 a low, fast car, often with a roof that can be folded back (6,3, *noun*)
6 pretty and attractive-looking (4, *adjective*)
7 soft, loose trousers and top that some people wear in bed (7, *noun*)
8 dirty and untidy (7, *adjective*)
9 too colourful, bright or expensive-looking (6, *adjective*)
10 with a confident, fashionable and expensive appearance (13, *adjective*)
11 (of a colour) strong and easy to see (6, *adjective*)
12 done in the same way for a long time (11, *adjective*)
13 An object in the home which is there because it is attractive rather than useful (8, *noun*)
14 using very simple ideas or patterns (used of rooms or interiors) (10, *adjective*)
15 not following the usual rules of how people normally think, dress, behave, etc. (14, *adjective*)
16 (of furniture / jewellery, etc.) made a long time ago and therefore valuable (7, *adjective*)
17 a French word used in English to mean fashionable and expensive (4, *adjective*)
18 (of a room) filled with too many things so it looks untidy (9, *adjective*)
19 a type of casual shoe, originally worn for playing sports (8, *noun*)
20 belonging to the present time (12, *adjective*)

b) Answer the mystery question in the column in the middle.

Words with several meanings

2 The words in the boxes all have more than one meaning. Read the definitions, then decide which of the meanings applies to each example sentence. Then write the appropriate number in the brackets, as in the example.

pretty *adv (spoken) / adj* **1** *adv* fairly, though not very **2** *adj* (of a woman, child or object) good-looking but not really beautiful
a *Georgetown is a **pretty** little seaside town with a charming town square and some attractive restaurants on the beach.* [*2*]
b *It's **pretty** obvious that we won't have many more visitors today.* [*1*]

class *n* **1** [C] the social group that someone belongs to according to job, wealth, family, etc. **2** [C] a group of pupils in a school who are taught together **3** [C] a group or category into which people or things are divided, according to their qualities **4** [U] *informal* exceptional style or skill when you do something
c *Vanessa and I have been best friends ever since we were in the same **class** at school.* [ ]
d *Financial cut-backs mean that all company executives are now expected to fly economy **class**.* [ ]
e *The move leading to Roberto's seventy-third minute goal showed real **class**.* [ ]
f *The University aims to encourage more applications from students with a working-**class** background.* [ ]

cool *adj / verb* **1** adj pleasantly low in temperature, but not cold **2** calm and in control **3** *informal* fashionable, attractive **4** *verb* to become less hot **5** not as friendly as expected
g *Your engine's overheated. Let it **cool** down for a while before you restart it.* [ ]
h *The I-Zone is a good place to pick up a **cool** pair of sunglasses to wear on the beach.* [ ]
i *Although the temperatures outside can be high, the hotel's air-conditioning keeps things nice and **cool**.* [ ]
j *My girlfriend has been decidedly **cool** towards me ever since I told her I was going on holiday with someone else.* [ ]
k *The job is a hectic and demanding one, so we need someone who can remain **cool** under extreme pressure.* [ ]

thing *n* **1** [C] object **2** [C] characteristic of someone or something **3** (*plural*) equipment, clothes, etc. **4** [C] action **5** (*plural*) the general situation, outlook
l *A self-heating frying pan? There's no such **thing**!* [ ]
m *The weather's bound to be good, so don't forget to pack your swimming **things**.* [ ]
n *Jay lay awake all night wondering whether he'd done the right **thing**.* [ ]
o ***Things** have been very quiet in the flat since Phil left for Australia.* [ ]
p *The **thing** I find really annoying about Justin is that he's so disorganised.* [ ]

hot *adj* **1** at a high temperature **2** (of food) containing pepper or chilli, giving it a very spicy taste **3** controversial **4** popular or fashionable at a particular moment
q *Some of the food in Thailand makes liberal use of spices and may be a little too **hot** for Western tastes.* [ ]
r *Latino singer Tony Ramirez is said to be the **hottest** property in show business right now.* [ ]
s *Government corruption is still likely to be a **hot** topic when the general elections come around next year.* [ ]
t *There was only enough **hot** water for one person to have a shower.* [ ]

tough *adj* **1** difficult to do or deal with, and needing a lot of effort and determination **2** able to live through difficult or severe conditions **3** very determined or strict **4** difficult to cut or chew
u *My steak is so **tough** I can hardly eat it.* [ ]
v *You need to be **tough** to survive life in the desert.* [ ]
w *Life during the war was extremely **tough** for the majority of people.* [ ]
x *The government has promised to be **tough** on crime.* [ ]

Patterns to notice

Adding emphasis with auxiliaries

3 Look at the mini-conversations below. Change the phrases in bold to give them more emphasis. Use the words in brackets, and an appropriate inversion or auxiliary.

A: I just met Carla in the street ... and that was fifteen minutes ago. **That woman can talk** (*Wow* + inversion) (1) *Wow, can that woman talk*. I thought she'd never stop!

B: Yeah, she goes on, (*certainly* + auxiliary) (2) .... a bit, that's true.

A: **It's hot** (*Boy* + inversion) (3) .... out there! It must be 35°. **I am glad** (inversion) (4) .... we've got a fridge full of nice, cold ... Huh? WHERE ARE THEY?

B: Ah, yes, I meant to tell you about that. I had some friends over earlier and we all got a bit thirsty. **I apologise** (*really* + auxiliary) (5) .... I'll get some more later.

A: You'll never guess who I met at work today ...

B: Who?

A: Whitney Spearmint. **She looked** (*Man* + auxiliary + inversion) (6) .... gorgeous!

B: **I think** (*really* + auxiliary) (7) .... it's about time you stopped inventing stories about meeting pop stars, Martin. After all, you are nearly 30 and you work in a Post Office.

A: **I've got** (*Boy* + inversion) (8) .... news for you!

B: What is it, what is it?

A: Well, you know that prize draw you entered ...

B: I've won! And you lent me the money for the ticket. Listen, **I appreciate** (*really* + auxiliary) (9) .... what you did ... I'll never forget it.

Grammar: adverbs

Position of adverbs

4 Read the joke and put the adverbs and adverbial phrases in the box below in the correct place.

~~angrily~~ for a few moments three times definitely never honestly desperately On the 12th, 13th and 14th of October on October 11th last year

The judge looked *angrily* at the prisoner in the dock.

'So you admit breaking into Carla's Fashion Store?' he said.

'Yes, your honour. But I can say I haven't done anything like this before, and it will happen again. I only did it because my wife needed a new dress.'

The judge looked at his case notes.

'I see. So why then did you break into the shop again?'

'Because my wife made me change the dress.'

Adverbs of manner with and without *-ly*

5 Underline the correct form to complete each sentence.

a It was nearly 1 o'clock, and we were *desperate* / *desperately* trying to contact my family to tell them where we were.
b Something smells *good* / *well*. What's for dinner?
c The mining company had to dig *deep* / *deeply* underground in order to extract the remaining coal.
d I have to admit that Ellen does look very *good* / *well* in her black dress.
e We'll only get the contract if we all work extra *hard* / *hardly* over the next few weeks.
f It's a pity you didn't complete the course. *Still* / *Already*, I imagine you learned quite a lot from it.
g You'd better give Tom and Barbara a ring to tell them we might be a bit *late* / *lately*.
h As I sat down, someone I'd never seen before waved to me *friendly* / *in a friendly way*.
i Many people think – *wrong* / *wrongly* I believe – that a change of government will have a positive effect on the economy.
j Although oil prices have risen considerably, this has *already* / *yet* to be reflected in the price of petrol.
k The presidential candidate walked *free* / *freely* among the crowds, smiling and shaking hands.
l I was expecting the delivery on Friday: it's now Tuesday and it *still* / *yet* hasn't arrived.

Focusing adverbs

6 Complete the sentences with *even*, *especially* or *only* in space 1 or 2.

a (1) .... Tony was so keen to come with us he (2) ....*even*........ offered to pay for the taxi.
b We're all keen on computer games: (1) .... Marta , who seems to spend her life (2) .... in front of a computer screen.
c My grandmother is the (1) .... person in my family who remembers (2) .... the war.
d (1) .... Jon is so lazy he doesn't (2) .... get out of bed before 1 o'clock.
e The weather was (1) .... bad in October, when it (2) .... rained almost every day.
f We were (1) .... so poor in those days, we couldn't (2) .... afford to buy shoes.
g Russia is the (1) .... European country with a population of (2) .... over 100 million people.
h Things (1) .... got so bad at work, I (2) .... considered resigning.
i I like all pasta dishes, (1) .... spaghetti, which I'd say is my (2) .... favourite.

Adverbs of probability

7 The Press are interviewing Candice de Berg about her latest film, *Star Time*. In the interview, replace the sentences with the adverb of probability closest in meaning.

definitely almost certainly undoubtedly most likely probably conceivably ~~possibly~~ definitely not

Question: Will you be making any more films in England?
Answer: It's possible – I'm not sure yet. (1 ....*possibly*.............)
Question: Has this been a fun film to work on?
Answer: This is definite. (2 ....)
Question: Do you think you will work with director Martin Biggins again?
Answer: This is 90% certain. (3 ....)
Question: Would you say that Biggins is good to work with?
Answer: There is no doubt about this. (4 ....)
Question: Will you be returning to London in the near future?
Answer: This is likely to happen. (5 ....)
Question: Do you think your role as a single mother in *Star Time* will attract a lot of controversy?
Answer: This is probable. (6 ....)
Question: Would you like to direct films one day?
Answer: I can imagine that happening but it's not very likely. (7 ....)
Question: There are rumours that you are romantically linked with co-star Harry Blunt. Are they true?
Answer: There is absolutely no chance of this. (8 ....)

Listen and read

Extract from a biography of Nicole Kidman

8 **a)** [8.1] Starting as a child actress in her native Australia, Nicole Kidman is now one of Hollywood's most recognisable faces. Read and / or listen to the extract from her autobiography.

Nicole Kidman

1 A single working mother in her mid-thirties, Nicole Kidman could now either slip into career apathy or forge ahead stubbornly. It will surprise no one that she opted for the latter, and quite spectacularly so. As she carved out a new persona, complete with both feminist and romantic overtones, not to mention a major image overhaul, the world took the courageous actress to its heart. Almost by default, the divorcee became an inspirational role model for women everywhere.

2 Setting out to prove the point that she could get along just fine without her husband, yet admitting on occasion that she was struggling to cope, Nicole's frankness was refreshing and appealing in equal measure. She never stopped giving interviews and her gradual acceptance of her new life could be clearly traced as the year progressed.

3 After eleven years of wearing flat shoes to avoid towering over Tom Cruise, the statuesque star famously charmed her public by gleefully giggling 'I can wear heels now!' when quizzed on the benefits of being single. Suddenly she became a style icon for a new generation.

4 Clothes shopping with girlfriends was now one of her favourite pursuits. But Nicole's sartorial tastes hadn't actually changed all that much from the days she spent trawling round flea markets[1]. 'I think clothes are creative. It's wonderful when someone like John Galliano has the ability to change the way people think of clothes or how they dress on a global level. Fashion is incredibly relevant. There's something admirable about boldness, because with boldness comes the opportunity to fail. But it's becoming harder now, because when you fail, people judge it so severely.'

5 A practical mum, Nicole is a 'bike shorts and sloppy joe' person around the house. 'It's like leading two different lives,' she jokes. 'I have my life, then I have this sort of fantasy life – going to premieres and putting on make-up and beautiful dresses.'

6 Thanks to all the extra exposure with *Moulin Rouge!*, *The Others* and also her very public divorce, Nicole's eclectic taste in clothes, her paleness and her long-legged figure have become fashionable, something which she finds most amusing. 'Believe me, my body is only OK,' she laughs. 'I get by, but it's not great. I have a boy's body, and I would rather look like a girl. *Moulin Rouge!* was all about corsets and padding.'

[1] markets where old or used goods are sold

b) Which paragraph deals with:

1 her feelings about clothes and fashion? ....4......
2 how she dealt with the media in the period after her divorce? ....
3 how she feels about being a style icon? ....
4 how the public reacted to her after her divorce? ....
5 the difference between her public and private lives? ....
6 the positive aspects of becoming single? ....

Check your pronunciation

9 a) [8.2] Listen again to this extract from the text. Pause at the points indicated and look at the *Pronunciation points* below.

1 A single working mother in her mid-thirties (1), Nicole Kidman could now either slip into career (2) apathy or forge ahead stubbornly. It will surprise no one (3) that she opted for the latter, and quite
5 spectacularly so. As she carved out a new persona, complete with both feminist and romantic overtones, not to mention a major image (4) overhaul, the world took the courageous actress to its heart. Almost by default, the divorcee became an inspirational role (5)
10 model for women everywhere.

LOOK!

Pronunciation points

1 Note the /ɜː/ in *thirties*. The sound is also found in *working* (line 1) and *world* (line 7).
2 Note that the stress is on the last syllable in *career*. Other two-syllable words stressed in this way are the name *Nicole* (line 2), *ahead* (line 3), *surprise* (line 3), *complete* (line 6), *default* (line 9) and *divorcee* (line 9).
3 Notice the /w/ sound that links *no* and *one*. The same linking sound is heard in *now either* (line 2) and *to its* (line 8).
4 Notice the pronunciation of the word *image* with two /ɪ/ sounds. The same sounds are heard in *women* (line 10).
5 Notice the /əʊ/ sound in *role*. The same sound is heard in *no one* (line 3), *so* (line 5), *persona* (line 5), *both* (line 6), *romantic* (line 6), *overtones* (line 6), *overhaul* (line 7) and *almost* (line 8).

b) Practise reading the passage yourself, paying attention to the *Pronunciation points* above. Use the recording to help you if necessary.

Wordspot

look, sound, feel

10 Find a word / words to complete the sentence or answer the question.

a According to the proverb, what should you do before you leap? ......look.........
b If you're feeling happy and optimistic, you're feeling on top of the ....
c What kind of look might you give someone to show you are angry or disapproving? ....
d If you express your feelings about something angrily, you sound .... about it.
e Artificially-created noises which are used in the theatre are called sound ....
f You call someone who closely resembles a celebrity a ....
g The person who watches for policemen while a crime is carried out is a ....
h If you feel both positively and negatively about something, what kind of feelings do you have? ....
i Someone who watches or observes an event is an ....
j The recorded music for a film is called the ....
k What phrasal verb means to respect or admire? Look .... to.
l What expression with *feel* is a way of giving permission? Feel ....
m What are phrases or slogans often used by journalists and politicians? ....
n What kind of movie makes you contented and happy? ....

Pronunciation

Silent letters

11 **a)** Look at the lists of words below. Underline the odd one out in each case. (Tip: look for silent letters.)

1 bribe comb eyebrow object
2 arrangement intriguing league reign
3 exhausted hundred hardly horror
4 dislike knowledge shock strike
5 animal film palm ridiculous
6 apricot clip psychedelic spokesman
7 castle insect topic tough
8 away eyebrow onwards wrong

b) [8.3] Listen to the words and check your answers.

c) [8.4] Read and listen to the headlines. Cross out the silent examples of the letter at the top of each headline.

1 H

Hundreds of vehicles in rush-hour queues

2 W

World-famous writer answers his critics

3 G

Foreign minister resigns after campaign of rumours

4 K

Unknown striker set to make debut due to Beckham's knee injury

5 L

Half of the world's wild salmon could die out

6 T

Queen to spend Christmas at Windsor Castle

7 P

Tax investigators find missing receipts in cupboard

d) Practise saying the headlines yourself. Use the recording to help you.

Check your writing

Unusual punctuation

12 **a)** The sentences below all feature an unusual aspect of pronunciation. Match the rule to the examples a)–f) below.

LOOK!

1 We use single inverted commas to indicate that a word is not being used in its usual sense, or is used sarcastically.
2 We use a hyphen in compound adjectives with *well* and *badly* when they come before the noun.
3 Asterisks are often used to replace the letters when we write a word which is possibly offensive.
4 Capital letters are used with greetings and signing-off phrases in letters and emails.
5 Capital letters are used for someone's job written at the end of an email or letter.
6 A single exclamation mark is used after phrases which indicate strong feelings or surprise.

a a well-cut classic suit. ...2.....
b a shirt with a 'loud' psychedelic pattern. ....
c She doesn't have to kick the **** out of a motorcycle gang to be cool. ....
d Narinder Ray
Human Resources Manager ....
e Regards
Veronica ....
f ripped jeans and a gaudy bright pink top covered in gold stars! ....

b) Add appropriate punctuation to the following sentences.

1 Roger is a very well built young man.
2 I just couldn't believe my ears.
3 Would you invest half a month's salary on a single item of clothing?
4 yours sincerely,
Terry Adams
marketing manager
5 There are too many badly designed clothes at this year's exhibition.
6 To my complete amazement, she turned round and called me a stupid ....
7 dear Mr Attley,
8 An example of their hospitality was shouting at me for losing my key.

Do you remember?

Pages 76-77

1 **The title of the module is *A Question of* ………………… .**

2 **Which word means: *filled with too many things so it looks untidy*? …………………**

3 **What three things are mentioned that you can have pierced? ………………… ………………… …………………**

4 **What do the following adjectives relate to?**
a antique …………………
b abstract …………………
c well-cut …………………

5 **What adjective is used to describe both a cuddly toy and cartoon characters? …………………**

6 **Which words come before the colours?**
a ………………… purple b ………………… green

Pages 78-79

7 **Frank Sinatra, Audrey Hepburn, Madonna and James Dean are described as *style* ………………… .**

8 **According to the quote, what did Audrey Hepburn do as discreetly as she dressed? …………………**

9 **Which is the correct alternative?**
He was *a simple* / *a simply* / *simply a* genius.

10 **What nouns do these adjectives go with?**
a a rare …………………
b personal …………………
c an entire …………………

11 **Which phrasal verb meaning *to survive a difficult experience* occurs twice in the text? …………………**

12 **Rearrange the words to form a sentence.**
a girl / do / find / like / look / people / offensive?/ does / Why / who / a girl
……………………………………………………………

Pages 80-81

13 **Which is the correct spelling?**
sound *affects* / *effects* / *iffects*

14 **What word goes before *free* and *good*? …………………**

15 **In the song, what were the *clouds in my coffee*? …………………**

16 **Which of the adjectives expresses a positive idea?**
a conceited b egotistical c immoral
d intriguing e shallow

17 **Which of these words is not an adverb?**
a constantly b instantly c lovely d naturally

18 **Which is the correct place for the time adverbial: (1), (2) or (3)?**
She (1) … was (2) …. quite naïve (3) .. when she met the man. (still)

Pages 82-83

19 **The task is to prepare a ………………… about something you hate.**

20 **What is the title of the British TV programme on which the task is based? …………………**

21 **Complete the three sentences.**
a It gets on my ………………… .
b I can't ………………… it.
c It just ………………… me absolutely mad.

22 **What phrasal verb means: *to connect someone by telephone*? …………………**

23 **Which *-ly* words come before the following?**
a …………………ly furious
b …………………ly superior
c …………………ly life

24 **What single word means: *an item of clothing*? …………………**

Pages 84-85

25 **What aspects of Anita Fernand's clothes and appearance do these adjectives describe?**
a ripped ……………………… b gaudy bright pink, covered in gold stars ………………………
c huge ………………………

26 **How does Narinder's letter begin?**
a Dear Miss Fernand b Dear Mrs Fernand
c Dear Ms Fernand

27 **How does Narinder end the letter?**
a Yours faithfully b Yours sincerely
c Yours truly

28 **Which adjective means: *unusual* or *attractive in a way that you notice*? ………………………**

29 **Which word follows *amazingly* or *funnily* to emphasise that something is surprising or coincidental? ………………………**

30 **Choose the correct form to complete the sentence.**
All *being* / *is* / *to be* / *will be* well, she'll be out of hospital by the end of the week.

module 9

Vocabulary

How technology will change our lifestyle

1 **a)** Find the right word in the box to complete the collocations.

~~conferencing~~ deserted freelance health isolation skilled interaction short-term labour-saving sedentary strain unskilled

Collocation		Definition
computer	(1) ...*conferencing*.........	a system whereby people can speak and communicate with others via a computer screen
highly-	(2)	with a high degree of training and experience
to work	(3)	to work independently for several different organisations
(4)	devices	machines which are designed to make physical work easier, e.g. dishwashers
(5)	contract	a contract which only guarantees work for a limited period of time
mental	(6)	the condition of your mind and your mental well-being
social	(7)	being without social contact with other people
put	(8)	on to impose exceptional difficulties on a relationship / resources, so that they suffer
(9)	wastelands	an area completely empty of people which is not used for anything
(10)	lifestyle	a way of life where you are usually sitting, and take little or no exercise
social	(11)	being with and talking to other people
(12)	workers	workers who have no specific training or skills

b) Complete the sentences with the appropriate form of the word in capitals.

1 The ..*unemployment*.. rate in this area is higher than the national average. **EMPLOY**
2 Statistics show that approximately 25% of American adults suffer from .... **OBESE**
3 You need .... to survive in today's changing labour market. **ADAPT**
4 After the accident, my brother had to endure a long period of .... while his broken leg healed. **ACTIVE**
5 People today are taking positive steps to improve their physical .... **FIT**
6 He has every imaginable .... in his kitchen. He must really enjoy cooking. **APPLY**
7 I don't think I want to play against her again. She's a very aggressive .... **OPPOSE**
8 It is becoming .... difficult to predict what technological changes are likely to occur in the next twenty years. **INCREASE**

Verb collocations

2 Which of the common verbs in the box below goes in each gap? Check the text in the Students' Book on pages 88–89 if necessary.

~~get~~ run make might leave think have know want give

a Even the experts don't always ......*get*....... it right.

b ... you need 200 times that amount of memory just to .... the company's software.

c They imagined the robots of the future would not only be able to .... for themselves, but ...

d ... all-in-one body suits ... did .... a number of fashion appearances ...

e Actually, we do now .... how to extend life – by eating less and exercising more.

f ... there's no need to .... your home / computer and traipse round the shops ...

g We simply refuse to .... up eating our nutritionally nightmarish fish and chips ...

h As for male pregnancy, I .... it filed under 'o' for 'only for the lunatic'.

i ... you .... well see genetic engineering for very specific and well-defined medical reasons ...

j ... what we .... is the best for our future generations.

3 **a)** Write the correct word or phrase next to the definition.

deluded device puddle double-glazing opt resounding ~~forego~~ outlook stack inclination ~~package~~ tuck

1 ...*package*.... (*noun*) a planned holiday arranged at a fixed price, which includes travel, hotels, meals, etc.
2 .... (*noun*) a small pool of water on a path, road, etc.
3 .... (*noun*) a piece of equipment designed for a particular purpose, such as recording or measuring something
4 .... (*verb*) to put things into a neat pile, one on top of the other
5 .... (*verb, formal*) to decide to not do or have something, especially something pleasurable
6 .... (*adjective*) made to believe something that is not true; deceived
7 .... [+ *for*] (*verb*) to choose one thing or course of action rather than another one
8 .... (*noun*) glass on a window or door in two separate panes with a space between them in order to keep heat in and noise out
9 .... [+ *into*] (*verb*) to put something into a small space so that it looks tidier or stays in place
10 .... (*noun*) a desire that makes you want to do something
11 .... (*noun*) what is expected to happen in the future
12 .... (*adjective*) very great or complete, so that many people know about it

b) Write the appropriate form of one of the words in the gaps.

1 We decided to .....*forego*..... the pleasures of the beach, and spend the day visiting some historic churches.
2 If you're too busy to make your own holiday arrangements, it might be easier for you to get a ....
3 Many kitchens nowadays contain a number of labour-saving ...., such as mixers and blenders.
4 I have absolutely no .... to move: I'm quite happy living where I am.
5 The show, which received excellent reviews when it opened, has proved to be a .... success with the public.
6 Anyone who thinks they are going to make money from such a ridiculous scheme must be seriously ....
7 I offered our guide a €10 note – he thanked me, and .... it discreetly into his top pocket.
8 My first job in the supermarket was to .... cans of tuna into an enormous pile.
9 After the torrential rain, there were several .... on the pitch, making it hard to play the ball along the ground.
10 The economic .... for the next few years is not especially good at the moment.
11 As the house is situated directly by the main road, we've installed .... to keep the noise down.
12 Everything on the menu looked very appetising, but in the end I decided to .... for the salmon in Champagne sauce.

Grammar: future forms

General

4 Underline the phrase which is closest in meaning to the phrase in bold.

1 There are probably no tickets left now, but **I'm willing to try**, if you like.
a I'll try b I'm going to try c I try

2 What I don't understand is why Helen **refuses to speak** to him.
a doesn't speak b won't speak
c isn't going to speak

3 **All the plans have been made for our flight to Jamaica.**
a We'll fly to Jamaica. b We fly to Jamaica.
c We're flying to Jamaica.

4 **The meal will be over** by the time we get there.
a They'll finish eating b They'll be eating
c They'll have finished eating

5 **I intend to be a lot more careful** next time I drive abroad.
a I'm going to be a lot more careful
b I shall be a lot more careful
c I'm being a lot more careful

6 **How about trying** a Japanese restaurant for a change?
a Will we try b Are we going to try
c Shall we try

7 **They'll be in the middle of their meal** at 8 o'clock, so I'll phone now.
a They'll eat b They're going to eat
c They'll be eating

8 **I'm very likely to see** Julia this afternoon – is there anything you want me to tell her?
a I'll probably see b I'll be seeing c I see

9 **Would you like me to** do the shopping?
a Am I going to b Will I c Shall I

10 Hmm ... let me think ... **I've just decided to cook** the meal if you go to the shops.
a I'll cook b I'm cooking c I'm going to cook

11 I'm not worried about making a fool of myself. **I'm prepared to dress up** if you want.
a I'm dressing up b I'm going to dress up
c I'll dress up

12 The new season **is timetabled to begin** at the beginning of September.
a begins b is beginning c will be beginning

'Future' phrases

5 Write sentences to complete the newspaper cuttings, using the word(s) in brackets.

Le Monde to print articles in English

France's most traditional newspaper, *Le Monde*, (1) ......is to print....... (be / print) a weekly supplement in English. Editor Jean-Marie Colombani announced that the first 12-page supplement of translated articles (2) .... (due / appear) next month.

Pirovsky to return to US

Controversial film director Ray Pirovsky (3) .... (verge / return) to the US 25 years after fleeing the country to escape criminal charges. Los Angeles police (4) .... (be / drop) the charges against Pirovsky, making his return a virtual certainty ...

Presidential victory in referendum

President Marref (5) .... (set / win) a landslide victory in a national referendum to grant him a five-year extension to his rule. Opinion polls indicate that approximately 85% of voters (6) .... (likely / vote) 'Yes' in next week's poll.

Bridge to link Sicily to Italy

Work (7) .... (about / begin) on a 5km-long bridge across the Straits of Messina connecting the island of Sicily to the Italian mainland. The project – first suggested some 30 years ago – is (8) '........................' (bound / benefit) the economy of the region, according to one prominent local politician.

Peace deal to end civil war

The government and the rebel SPLA group are (9) .... (point / reach) an agreement to end their 20-year civil war. The two sides (10) .... (be / sign) a temporary ceasefire which allows a degree of autonomy for those regions ...

Future in the past

6 Complete the text with words or phrases from the box below.

were on the point of would was to be ~~were supposed to~~ were leaving was going to be were going to be was about to say

Florence Bell

1 Florence Bell was born on the first day of 1900. As one of eight children, she left school at the age of 14. 'In those days, young girls (1) ...*were supposed to*.... help their mothers around the house,' she remembers. She
5 was never terribly keen on school anyway: 'It was very strict,' she says. 'I remember the headmistress bringing us all into her study, as we (2) .... school the next day. She said this (3) .... the worst day of our lives ...
10 I (4) .... "No it isn't, it's the best!", but I decided to keep quiet. You couldn't afford to be cheeky in those days.'

At the age of 16, she met Leslie Parsons, the man who (5) .... later become her
15 husband. After becoming engaged in 1918, they (6) .... getting married in 1920, when Leslie lost his job and the wedding had to be postponed. 'We always knew things (7) .... hard,' said Florence.
20 'Finding a job was very difficult in those days.' It was eight years before Leslie and Florence could finally afford to marry: soon afterwards they moved into the small terraced house in north London which (8) .... their home for the next
25 sixty-five years. Neither of them ever had any desire to move.

'Yes, I've enjoyed it on the whole. The only thing is, if I came back, I'd have a bit more money.'

Patterns to notice

Describing trends

7 a) Match the phrases 1–8 to their opposites in a–h.

1 get better
2 deteriorate
3 increase
4 rapidly
5 blurred
6 longer and longer
7 more and more (+ *plural noun*)
8 more and more (+ *adjective / uncountable noun*)

a clear
b decrease
c get worse
d fewer and fewer
e improve
f shorter and shorter
g less and less
h slowly

1 ...*c*... 2 .... 3 .... 4 ....
5 .... 6 .... 7 .... 8 ....

b) Rewrite the following sentences with the opposite of the phrase in bold.

1 This type of car is becoming **more and more** popular.
This type of car is becoming less and less popular.
2 The standard of teaching seems to be **getting better**.
....
....
3 The town's importance is **slowly increasing**.
....
....
4 **More and more** people are taking holidays abroad.
....
....
5 We have **less and less** time to ourselves these days.
....
....
6 Julio's English seems to be **slowly improving**.
....
....
7 The difference between the two groups is becoming **clearer and clearer**.
....
....
8 The days are getting **longer and longer**.
....
....

Listen and read

25 Signs You Live in the 21st Century

8 **a)** [9.1] Read and / or listen to the email.

25 Signs You Live in the 21st Century

1 You just tried to enter your password on the microwave.

2 You have a list of 15 phone numbers to reach your family of three.

3 You call your son's beeper to let him know it's time to eat. He emails you back from his bedroom, 'What's for dinner?'

4 Your daughter sells Girl Scout Cookies via her website.

5 You chat several times a day with a stranger from South Africa, but you haven't spoken with your next-door neighbour yet this year.

6 You check the ingredients on a can of chicken noodle soup to see if it contains echinacea[1].

7 Your grandmother asks you to send her a JPEG file of your newborn so she can create a screen saver.

8 You pull up in your own driveway and use your cell phone to see if anyone is home.

9 Every commercial on television has a website address at the bottom of the screen.

10 You buy a computer and six months later it is out of date and sells for half the price you paid.

11 Leaving the house without your cell phone, which you didn't have the first 20 or 30 years of your life, is cause for panic and turning around to go get it.

12 Using real money, instead of credit or debit cards, to make a purchase would be a hassle and take planning.

13 Cleaning up the dining room means getting the fast food bags out of the back seat of your car.

14 Your reason for not staying in touch with family is that they do not have email addresses.

15 You consider second-day air delivery painfully slow.

16 Your dining room table is now your flat filing cabinet.

17 Your idea of being organized is multiple-colored Post-it notes.

18 You hear most of your jokes via email instead of in person.

19 You get an extra phone line so you can get phone calls.

20 You disconnect from the Internet and get this awful feeling, as if you just pulled the plug on a loved one.

21 You get up in the morning and go online before getting your coffee.

22 You wake up at 2am to go to the bathroom and check your email on your way back to bed.

23 You start tilting your head sideways to smile. :)

24 You're reading this.

25 Even worse, you're going to forward it to someone else.

Send this page to a friend.

Read another email.

[1] a plant which is sometimes used to cure colds

b) Write the numbers of the signs which relate to these topics. They may relate to more than one category.

- computers in general .....1, 10...........
- email ....
- websites and chatting on the Internet ....
- telecommunications ....
- the way people eat and shop ....
- your home being like an office ....

Check your pronunciation

9 a) [9.2] Listen again to this extract from the text. Pause at the points indicated and look at the *Pronunciation points* below.

18 You hear most of your jokes via email instead of in person (1).

19 You get an extra phone line so you can get phone calls.

20 You disconnect from the Internet and get this awful (2) feeling, as if you just pulled the plug on a loved one.

21 You get up in the morning and go online (3) before getting your coffee.

22 You wake up at 2am to go to the bathroom and check your email on your way back to bed. (4)

23 You start tilting your head sideways to smile. :)

24 You're reading this. (5)

25 Even worse, you're going to forward it to someone else.

LOOK!

Pronunciation points

1. Notice the /ɜː/ sound in *person*. The same sound occurs in *worse* (point 25).
2. Notice the /ɔː/ sound in *awful*. This also occurs in *morning* (point 21) and *forward* (point 25).
3. Notice the way the words *go* and *online* are linked with a /w/ sound. The same thing occurs in *2am* (point 22).
4. Notice the many words pronounced with weak forms in this sentence: *you*, *at*, *to*, *to*, *the*, *and*, *your*, *your* and *to* are all pronounced with a schwa /ə/ sound.
5. Notice the stress on *this* because this is the important part of the sentence.

b) Practise reading the passage yourself, paying attention to the *Pronunciation points* above. Use the recording to help you if necessary.

Wordspot

well

10 Complete the sentences with a word or phrase that goes with *well*.

a Unfortunately for Simon, the interview didn't ......*go*......... at all well.

b I hope you .... well. Breakfast will be served in about fifteen minutes.

c The report you sent in was extremely clear and thorough, Kate. Well ....!

d .... well .... being a talented gymnast, Ian is also an excellent footballer.

e After Lisa finishes her exams, she and her friends are flying off to Greece for a well-................. holiday.

f I think we .... well see a little bit of rain before the end of the day.

g Thanks for the game. Well ....! You deserved to win.

h I'm well .... of what people are saying about us, but I still believe it's none of their business.

i If you happen to visit Dublin, the Castle is well .... visiting.

j My mother has been very touched by the number of .... well .... cards she's received following her operation.

k Having invested her inheritance wisely, Jane could now consider herself reasonably well ....

l You let my sister buy a video. Can't I have one .... well?

m Even though it was well .... midnight, everyone was fast asleep.

n Although I have no doubt it was a very well-................. comment, I think you may have unintentionally caused offence.

o Few people now remember Bob Bachman, but he was well-................. as a TV entertainer in the 1970s.

p I was very impressed by little Adam's politeness: he really is a very well- .... young man.

Pronunciation

Intonation in interjections

11 a) [9.3] Listen to the phrases below. What does the phrase in bold express?

- annoyance
- doubt
- interest / surprise
- acceptance of a situation

1 A: It seems that David has changed his mind again. Now Chris wants *you* to do the presentation.
B: **Well, well** ... how odd ... thought he wanted to do it himself. ..interest / surprise..

2 A: Surely, you have to agree that *Monty's* is the best restaurant in town. Don't you agree?
B: **Well**, there are plenty of other restaurants where the food is very good. Take *Mario's*, for example ...
....

3 A: Oh dear, the film's already started.
B: **Well**, that's just your hard luck. You should have got here earlier, shouldn't you?
....

4 So Florence, you've decided to leave us. **Well**, there's nothing more I can do to persuade you to stay, so good luck.
....

5 **Well**, that's the last time I eat in *that* restaurant.
....

6 **Well**, I never thought I'd see the day when Georgie wore a tie.
....

7 **Well**, we'll just have to drink water if there isn't any Coke.
....

8 **Well**, from what I've seen of your work up to now, I'd say there's very little chance of you passing. ....

b) Practise saying the phrases yourself. Pay particular attention to the pronunciation of *well*.

Check your writing

Introductory phrases

12 a) The introductory phrases below are used in the text *What didn't come to pass* on pages 88-89 of the Students' Book. Match the phrases in the box below with the reasons for their use.

actually Take ... for example ~~Face it, ...~~ ~~True, ... but ...~~ For instance, ... Fortunately for ... Which brings me to ... It's my bet that ... as for ...

1 to persuade the reader to accept something they don't want to be true, or don't know about ....face it...........
2 to accept that something is correct, before introducing a counter-argument ....
3 to introduce an example ....
4 to introduce a change of subject, or a new topic ....
5 to introduce a personal opinion ....
6 to indicate that someone has been lucky ....

b) Improve the paragraphs below by using one of the introductory phrases from the box to fill the gaps (some of the phrases have been split).

Many people think that congestion in cities would be eased my making all public transport free of charge. (1) ....True..........., such a scheme would have many advantages, (2) ....but.............. there are a number of problems to be considered as well. (3) ...., wouldn't the buses and trains become so overcrowded that it would be impossible to get on? (4) ...., nobody likes to be squashed up against their fellow citizens, and (5) .... people would soon return to their cars ...

People often think shopping online is an easy way of getting your shopping done where you want and when you want, but (6) ...., things aren't always perfect in practice. (7) .... the problem of delivery times, (8) .... How do you know you'll happen to be at home when the delivery man rings the bell with your long-awaited goodies? And (9) .... getting the exact thing you ordered, that can be a whole new nightmare ...

Presently, the little village can only be reached after a two-day trek through the mountains. (10) .... those of you who find the idea of spending two days on horseback a bit too much, a new road is being built: (11) .... the main problem with this kind of eco-tourism – however much we may think we can preserve the real character, change is inevitable once the tourists arrive.

Do you remember?

Pages 86-87

1 Complete the titles of two of the texts.
a *The '....................' House*
b *Behind the* ....

2 Which phrasal verb means: *to become popular and fashionable*? ....

3 Which phrase comes before both the words *meeting* and *headset*? ....

4 Supply the missing prepositions.
Skilled professionals will be (1).................... pressure to work longer hours, while the mundane work will be done (2) .... machine, leading (3).................... high unemployment.

5 Why will there be no 'jobs for life' in the future?
....

6 What is the noun form of these adjectives?
a inactive ....
b isolated ....
c adaptable ....

Pages 88-89

7 Complete the title of the article: *What didn't* ....

8 Who said in 1981: *640k of memory ought to be enough for anyone*? ....

9 What phrase goes in the gaps?
But what have we got ? More (1).................... devices and less (2).................... .

10 What, according to the article, are the two keys to extending life? ....

11 Which word completes this sentence?
The first artificial eyes are .... to appear within ten years.

12 Rearrange the words to form a sentence.
that / will / 2020 / by / have / predicted / cash / disappeared / is / virtually / It
....
....

Pages 90-91

13 Complete the title: *The Changing* .... *of Tourism*

14 What can you search for in the Argentine desert?
....

15 What are the missing countries?
a A bird watching holiday in remote Eastern ....
b A horse-riding holiday in the olive groves of Northern ....

16 What word comes after *painting, Italian cookery* and *survival*? ....

17 What adjective means: *unclear* or *difficult to see*?
....

18 Rearrange the letters to form two verbs describing change.
a mivoper ....
b etedroarite ....

Pages 92-93

19 The task is to create a time capsule for whom?
....

20 What examples of everyday objects are given?
....

21 What adjective means *unusual* or *surprising*?
....

22 In what year will the time capsule be opened?
....

23 What will the time capsule be the size of?

24 Put the verbs into the correct form.
[It] can (1) .... (seal) so effectively that even fresh food (2).................. (preserve) perfectly.

Pages 94-95

25 Name three phrases with *well* which are used to congratulate someone.
....

26 What word combines with *well* to mean:
a wealthy? ....
b muscular? ....
c polite? ....

27 What is the opposite of *well ahead*? ....

28 What are the missing prepositions?
a print .... a document
b type .... your password
c click .... an icon

29 Which of these words does not go with *hard*?
a copy b file c question d ware

30 What are the three things mentioned that you can do with an email? ....
....

module 10

Vocabulary

When is it OK to lie?

1 a) Answer the questions using a word beginning with the letter shown.

1 What B means false, or intended to deceive people (*adjective*)? ...bogus.......
2 What B is how you speak if you tell the truth even if it upsets others (*adverb*)? ....
3 What C means to get money by telling people something which is false (*verb*)? ....
4 What C means to be unfaithful to your partner (*phrasal verb*)? ....
5 What E means you make something much bigger or more important than it really is (*verb*)? ....
6 What E is the reason people give for having done something wrong (*noun*)? ....
7 What F is a small, unimportant lie (*noun*)? ....
8 What F is a document, painting or bank note which is not real, but intended to deceive people (*noun*)? ....
9 What G means to escape without punishment (*phrasal verb*)? ....
10 What G is malicious talk about other people (*noun*)? ....
11 What H is an elaborate attempt to make people believe something that isn't true (*noun*)? ....
12 What Hs do you tell when someone needs to realise some unpleasant facts about themselves (*noun, plural*)? ....
13 What O is a formal and serious promise you take, e.g. in a court of law (*noun*)? ....
14 What P is lying under O (*noun*)? ....
15 What Rs are pieces of information being passed around which may or may not be true (*noun, plural*)? ....
16 What S means to make something more widely known and is often used with Rs (*verb*)? ....
17 What T means that you have been lied to and deceived by someone else (*phrasal verb*)? ....
18 What Ts are stories which you tell the teacher to get others into trouble (*noun*)? ....
19 What T means to make a formal statement in a court of law (*verb*)? ....
20 What W is the colour of lies which are told to protect people or avoid harm (*adjective*)? ....

b) Use the correct form of one of the words in part a) to complete the sentences.

1 Dutchman Hans van Meegeren made a fortune from selling paintings, supposedly by Dutch masters like Vermeer. In fact, the paintings were all ....forgeries... which he did himself!
2 When Bernard said he'd been to the United States hundreds of times, I'm sure he was ....: it can't be more than five or six.
3 The accused swore under .... that he spent the evening at home watching videos: this was later found to be a lie, and he was charged with ....
4 Henry has been trying to .... people out of money by persuading them to invest in a .... insurance scheme.
5 Kirsty says that Robbie made her cry by pulling her hair, but I suspect she's telling ....
6 The robbers might have .... if they hadn't left one vital clue at the scene of the crime.
7 Rather than tell little Hannah the truth about what happened to her cousin, we decided to tell her a ....
8 I'm so annoyed that they have been .... about my private life. It's none of their business.
9 David spoke very ...., and told us a lot of ...., which upset many people but was probably necessary.
10 There have been a lot of .... going round about redundancies. Can you confirm or deny them?
11 Rogers made a number of phone calls claiming to have planted bombs: they were all ...., and nothing was ever found.
12 Everyone knew that Angus had been .... on his wife for years: unfortunately she was the last to know.
13 I hope you've got a good .... for being three hours late for dinner.
14 I had to tell a few .... to get the day off – but I'm sure no one will mind.
15 Hanson was a very convincing liar, and many people were .... by him.

Patterns to notice

Patterns with *as* ... *as* + verb

2 Write a phrase with *as* ... *as* + verb that is similar in meaning to the phrase in bold.

a I phoned my mother **at the earliest opportunity**. ..as soon as I could...
b Take **all the time you require** to finish the report ... there's no hurry. ....
c Now you can talk for **an unlimited period** thanks to BT's new Talk Line mobile phone deal. ....
d According to the Beaumont Diet, you can eat **an unlimited quantity of pasta** – but don't put any sauce on it! ....
e Although the weather wasn't great, we went to the beach **whenever it was possible**. ....
f John drove up the motorway **at maximum speed** – which wasn't very fast in such an old car. ....
g I recommend that you sleep **the maximum number of hours possible** during the bus journey, as you'll have to start work early tomorrow. ....
h Help yourself to **all the chocolates you want**. I can't eat them. ....
i Jane did **the maximum amount of work possible** in the short time she had available. ....
j I phone my sister **at every possible opportunity**, although phoning South Africa can be very expensive. ....
k We had **no time limit** to make the recordings. ....
l Apparently, you can drive **without speed restrictions** on private roads. ....
m We'll send a taxi **when there is one available**. ....
n You can take **all the money you require** from the cash box. ....
o Although my aunt lives hundreds of miles away, I go to visit **every time I am able to**. ....
p They promised to come and finish the work **when it was possible for them to**. ....

Grammar: noun phrases

Articles

3 Complete the one-liners (short jokes) with *a*, *an*, *the* or *ø*.

One Liners

(1) ...ø..... women are to blame for all (2) .... lies (3) .... men tell – they will keep asking (4) .... questions.

(5) .... people who cough loudly never go to (6) .... doctor's. They go to (7) .... cinema.

What's (8) .... best way to get (9) .... youthful figure?
Ask (10) .... woman her age.

(11) .... man knows he's in (12) .... love when he loses interest in his car for (13) .... few days.

(14) .... library at (15) .... White House has been burned down. Apparently (16) .... President is very upset. Some of (17) .... books hadn't been coloured in yet.

You know you're getting old when you have (18) .... birthday party, and (19) .... candles cost more than (20) .... cake.

What's (21) .... secret of (22) .... happiness? Give me my golf clubs, (23) .... fresh air, and (24) .... beautiful partner. Then keep (25) .... golf clubs and (26) .... fresh air.

Demonstratives and possessive adjectives

4 Complete the text with words from the box below.

it's that (x 4) ~~this~~ its (x 2) their those (x 2) these their own (x 2)

Aliens

According to some, (1) ......*this*......... will be the century when all (2) .... funny little aliens we first read about in the 1950s are finally going to make contact. Not so fast, say others: UFOs are all in the mind, and should be seen as a form of cultural hysteria. (3) ....'s the disappointing conclusion of British researchers Andy Roberts and David Clarke whose latest book investigates thousands of military reports into UFO sightings.

'Most of (4) .... early sightings date back to the 1950s – the period of the Cold War,' says Clarke. 'Remember that the threat of nuclear war hung over the world at (5) .... time. People naturally wanted to believe that something up there in the sky would come and rescue them.'

But (6) .... not just a question of psychology: technology comes into it as well. 'Our knowledge of radar systems – which pick up UFOs – was in (7) .... infancy then. The military radars were simply picking up (8) .... aeroplanes – and thinking they were UFOs. (9) .... days the number of incidents appearing on radar has dwindled to almost nothing. Surely (10) .... cannot be a coincidence,' argues Clarke.

Of course (11) .... won't convince the thousands who claim to have seen UFOs with (12) .... eyes. And, on the other side of the world, preparations are already being made for when humans and extra-terrestrials finally meet face-to-face. Officials in the town of Barra do Graças, in the swamps of Brazil's Matto Grosso, and a hotspot for sightings of UFOs, have already designated 12 acres to give the world (13) .... first UFO airport.

The Brazilian UFO Investigation Team also have (14) .... headquarters in nearby Pantanal. So the first human words our alien visitors hear may well be 'Ben vindos ao planeta terra'.

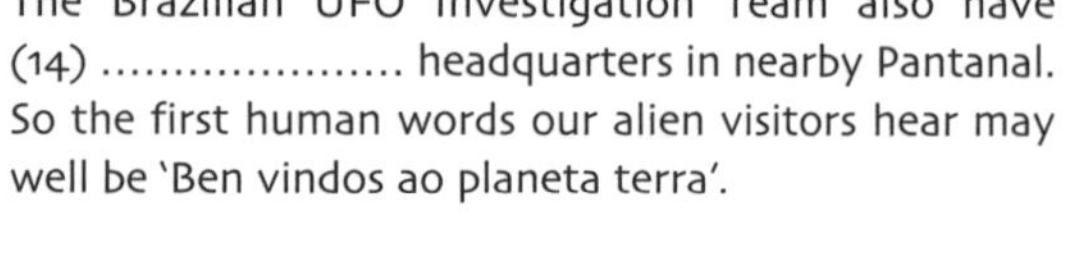

Quantifiers

5 Complete the sentences with a quantifier from the box below.

all any (x 2) ~~each~~ both every (x 2) few (x 2) a few (x 2) little no (x 4)

Fishy FACTS

a A starfish can be cut into a number of large chunks, and ....*each*..... piece will grow into a completely whole starfish.

b The cod lays vast numbers of eggs, but .... of them survive – about five out of .... million!

c Not .... sharks are dangerous. In fact the largest shark (the whale shark) eats only tiny plankton and has .... real teeth at all! Very .... people are actually killed by sharks.

d Some European eels leave their home rivers and use .... waterway they can find to make it to the Gulf of Mexico, where they lay their eggs – a distance of up to 6,000 miles! They can even travel .... metres by land if necessary.

e Oysters belong to .... sexes in their lifetime: after beginning life as a male, they can undergo sex changes from female to male!

f .... fish can live completely without water, but mudskippers (found in tropical swamps) often leave the water for .... hours to lie on the mud.

g Fish are found in virtually .... large body of water in the world – apart from the Dead Sea (between Israel and Jordan), where the salty water means that .... fish can survive.

h Although it's safe to say there are .... sea monsters, the giant sea squid – *architeuthis dux* – comes pretty close. Scientists still know .... about this 20–40ft squid, which has never been seen in its natural habitat; nor have .... deep-sea squid ever been caught alive.

Ellipsis and substitution

6 Cross out the unnecessary words in the dialogue. The number of words to be crossed out is shown at the end of each line. Hyphenated or contracted forms count as two words. In some cases you may need to add a word.

Lesley: ~~Be~~ careful! You nearly knocked over that poor cyclist. (–1)
Tony: I'm sorry. It's not easy to look at the road and the map at the same time. (–2)
Lesley: Well, I did offer to map-read but you wouldn't let me map-read. (–2)
Tony: Because you always get us lost. Or you did get us lost last time, anyway. (–3)
Lesley: No, I didn't get us lost! You wouldn't listen to me! (–3)
Tony: Never mind. Are there any more car sweets? Can I have a car sweet? (–3)
Lesley: No, you can't have a car sweet. You ate the last car sweet an hour ago. (–6)
Tony: It's a pity we didn't get some more car sweets when we stopped for petrol. (–5)
Lesley: Just a minute. Did that sign say *Crawley ten miles*?
Tony: I think it said *Crawley ten miles*. Why? (–5)
Lesley: Because it means we're going in the wrong direction!

Pronouns

7 Complete the sentences with a suitable pronoun. This could be a personal pronoun (*I*, *you*, *me*, etc.), a reciprocal pronoun (*each other*), a reflexive pronoun (*yourself*, *myself*, etc.) or a demonstrative pronoun (*this*, *that*, etc.).

a Although I've never been in that position ....*myself*...., I have a lot of sympathy for people who get into debt.
b I must admit that at times I find .... hard to get out of bed in the mornings.
c There are going to be roadworks for the next few weeks: apparently ....'re building a new roundabout.
d Thank heavens ....'s over! Now we can concentrate on something a bit livelier.
e I'm sure .... is going to come as a complete surprise to you all, but we've an announcement to make ...
f Upon entering the Cathedral, ... is struck by the enormous sense of space.
g Team work is vital: all the sales staff should be able to rely on .... 100%.
h It just goes to show. .... can't trust anyone nowadays.
i If you didn't spend so much time admiring .... in the mirror, we might not be late all the time!
j 'Can you two stop whispering please? This is a library.' 'Who? ....?'

Pronunciation

Weak and strong pronunciation of pronouns

8 **a)** [10.1] Pronouns are stressed if they are particularly important in the sentence. Listen to this example.

It was **you** who suggested that **we** invite **them** ... not **me**!

b) [10.2] Listen to the sentences below, paying attention to the pronouns in bold. Mark the ones that are stressed by underlining them.

1 **They** seem to have mentioned everyone except **me**.
2 The new medication has made **him** feel much better, but **it** didn't help **her** very much.
3 **You** might not want to see **him**, but **I** certainly do.
4 **I** just don't know what on earth **we** can tell **him** ... maybe your uncle can help.
5 If **you** see Andy again, ask **him** to call **me** instead of Mr Bernard.
6 **It**'s Frank who's the problem: if **we** could persuade **him**, the rest would be easy.
7 Apparently **they**'re going to ban cars in the town centre: what will **we** do then?
8 **It** doesn't matter what **she** thinks – **it**'s what **you** think that worries **me**.
9 **I** don't know about **you**, but **I**'ve had enough of this.
10 Was it **you** who **I** spoke to the other day?

c) Practise saying the sentences, copying the voices on the recording.

Listen and read

Believe it or not

9 **a)** [10.3] Read and / or listen to the articles below.

Believe it or not

A Brittney Pringle, a nine-month-old baby from Perth, Australia, made her parents rich the moment she spoke her first words. 'Brittney gave us a couple of goo-goos and ga-gas and then blurted out the numbers 9, 12, 14, 22, 31 and 39,' says proud mum, Dorcas Pringle. 'We ran out and bought the lottery ticket – and now our Brittney's going to grow up as the world's youngest self-made millionaire. I can't explain how she did what she did, but we are determined she's going to lead a normal life.'

B New Yorker Alvin Eykers is divorcing his wife Judith because her psychic powers put too much strain on their marriage. 'She'd finish my sentences before I got the words halfway out of my mouth,' says Eykers. 'I could never surprise her with a gift for Christmas or her birthday and I could never get away with even the littlest white lie. It was like she had a peephole into my mind.' The crisis came when Judith accused him of having an affair with his firm's receptionist. Eykers insists: 'I haven't touched her or even said two words to her – yet.'

C A British motorist lost her way during a day trip to Calais and drove 800 miles across Europe looking for somewhere to turn round. Vivienne Vanderwault-Hudson, who had been shopping for cigarettes and alcohol, headed down the motorway, crossed the Pyrenees into Spain, and didn't stop until Gibraltar. 'I get very scared driving – I've been stopped twice for driving too slowly. I kept hoping there would be a gap in the road, but there wasn't. So I decided to keep going.'

D An Ohio woman, Addie Crawley, got a shock when her ex-husband – who had been missing for 20 years – suddenly appeared from his cubbyhole hiding place in their former marital home. Thinking 48-year-old Ben Holmes was a ghost, Crawley drew her .22 handgun and shot him. He survived, later explaining in court that he had lived in the same house as his ex for several years, but hid himself whenever she was around. He had emerged to claim his share of the property.

E Novice climber Leonardo Diaz got stranded in a freak blizzard 12,500ft up in the Andes. The Colombian tried to call for help on his mobile phone, but discovered that his pay-as-you-go credit had run out. Just when he had resigned himself to freezing to death, he received a call – from a telemarketer at his phone company, wondering if he'd like to buy more minutes. Diaz explained the situation, and she alerted the emergency services. She and her colleagues then took turns to ring Diaz to keep his spirits up until help arrived seven hours later.

F An American housewife is offering psychic consultations to troubled pets. Carol Schultz, who claims she can speak the language of animals, charges $50 a session to counsel cats, dogs and horses. Satisfied customers include a dog which was Hitler in a past life and slept all the time to escape depression, and a dog which was trapped in a cat's body.

b) These articles all appeared in tabloid newspapers and **claim** to be true. Which stories do you think are true? Which do you think are made up?

Check your pronunciation

10 a) [10.4] Listen again to this extract from the text. Pause at the points indicated and look at the Pronunciation Points below.

1 Novice climber (1) Leonardo Diaz got stranded in a freak blizzard 12,500ft up in the Andes. The Colombian tried to
5 call for help on his mobile phone (2), but discovered that his pay-as-you-go credit had run out. Just when he had resigned himself to freezing to death, he
10 received (3) a call – from a telemarketer at his phone company, wondering (4) if he'd like to buy more minutes. Diaz explained the situation, and she
15 alerted the emergency (5) services. She and her colleagues then took turns to ring Diaz to keep his spirits up until help arrived seven hours later.

LOOK!

Pronunciation points

1 Notice that the letter 'b' in *climber* is not pronounced.
2 Note that the stress on this compound noun is on *phone*.
3 Notice the pronunciation of the *-ed* ending as /d/ here: the same as *tried* (line 4), *discovered* (line 6), *explained* (line 14) and *arrived* (line 19). Contrast this with the /ɪd/ pronunciation of *stranded* (line 2) and *alerted* (line 15).
4 Notice the /ʌ/ sound in the first syllable of *wondering*. It is also found in *Colombian* (line 4), *discovered* (line 6), *run* (line 7), *company* (line 12) and *up* (line 18).
5 Notice the stress is on the second syllable of *emergency*. *Colombian* (line 4) has the same stress pattern.

b) Practise reading the passage yourself, paying attention to the *Pronunciation points* above. Use the recording to help you if necessary.

Check your writing

Spelling

11 a) The verbs in the first column all feature in this module. Complete the table, using a dictionary to check the spelling if necessary.

infinitive	present participle	past tense
cry	*crying*	*cried*
lie (to someone)		
commit		
spit		
rely		
lay (out)		
grab		
die		

b) The words below also feature in the module. Write in the missing letters to give the correct spelling.

1 s u s p i *c* i o *u* s
2 i n s t _ n t a n _ _ u s
3 m a l i _ i _ u s
4 c o n t r _ v _ _ s _ _ l
5 e f _ i c _ _ n t _ y
6 r _ l _ a b l _
7 u n f a m _ _ i _ _
8 a d v _ _ t _ s _ m e _ _

c) Write the appropriate form of the word in capitals to complete the sentence.

1 We looked through every single job *advertisement* in the paper, without finding anything suitable. **ADVERTISE**
2 It is true that he hasn't .... any crime, but he certainly acted badly. **COMMIT**
3 There are currently some very .... proposals for a new law regarding unemployment benefit. **CONTROVERSY**
4 As he was ...., the King called all his followers to attend to him. **DIE**
5 The streets of the city are .... out in a simple grid pattern. **LAY**
6 There have been a number of .... rumours about Duncan appearing in the press. **MALICE**
7 It's very hard to get .... information about what's happening in the area as the telephone lines are down. **RELY**
8 The way that man has been hanging round outside the bank seems very .... to me. **SUSPECT**

Do you remember?

Pages 96-97

1 **What's the title of the module?** ....

2 **In the example of a *white lie*, where has the rabbit gone?** ....

3 **What are the missing words?**
Sorry, she's (1) .... a meeting (2) .... the moment.

4 **What phrasal verb means: *to escape without punishment*?** ....

5 **What verb goes with the nouns *forgery* and *perjury*?** ....

6 **Which of these words does not go with the verb *tell*?**
a a fib b home truths c a hoax d tales

Pages 98-99

7 **What animal did the man see in his garden?** ....

8 **According to the quotation, what is truth stranger than?** ....

9 **What are the missing adverbs in this quotation?**
It has (1) .... been desirable to tell the truth, but (2) ...., if (3) ...., necessary to tell the whole truth.

10 **In the story, who got dressed as fast as (s)he could?** ....

11 **Which is not a possible way to complete the sentence?**
Andy rides his motorbike as *fast* / *many* / *much* / *often* as he can.

12 **Complete the sentence.**
Words like *this, that, these* are (1) ....: *my, his, her*, etc., are (2) ...., and *some, no, a lot of*, etc., are (3) ....

Pages 100-101

13 **According to the test, if you're lying, do you spit out more or fewer grains of rice?** ....

14 **When were lie detectors first used in the USA?** ....

15 **Who or what is *your other half*?**
a the bad side of your personality
b your brother or sister
c your husband or wife

16 **What is the verb used to describe your face going red from embarrassment or shame?** ....

17 **What does the phrasal verb *hang on* mean?** ....

18 **What single word can replace the words in bold?**
A: Do they realise they are blushing?
B: No, I don't think they **realise they are blushing.**
....

Pages 102-103

19 **The task is to find out if your partner is** ....

20 **Which is the correct alternative?**
I once *have made* / *made* a record.

21 **Supply the missing modal verbs in these phrases.**
a You .... not believe this, but ...
b This one .... possibly be true.
c There's no way she .... have ...

22 **What words are used to emphasise that something is true?** ....

23 **Complete the sentence with the correct form.**
Do you really expect *that we will* / *us to* / *we* believe that?

24 **Which adjectives belong with these nouns?**
a .... people
b .... experiences
c .... relationships

Pages 104-105

25 **The adjectives *soggy* and *crumpled* are used to describe what?** ....

26 **Supply the missing prepositions in the sentences.**
a I heard children's voices .... the background.
b The rooms were all laid .... in the same way.
c One day he got caught ....

27 **Which of these is not mentioned in the texts?**
a CCTV b email c the Internet
d mobile phones e text messaging

28 **Rearrange the letters to form words ending in *-ly*.**
a burpymeals ....
b middleytat ....
c tilmetalyu ....

29 **Rearrange the words to form a sentence.**
believe / Do / expect / me / really / that? / to / you
....

30 **Which word is different in meaning?**
a amazing b joking c kidding

Pronunciation table

Consonants Symbol	Key Word	Vowels Symbol	Key Word
p	pan	iː	beat
b	ban	ɪ	bit
t	tip	e	bet
d	dip	æ	bat
k	cap	ɑː	bar
g	gap	ɒ	block
tʃ	church	ɔː	bought
dʒ	judge	ʊ	book
f	few	uː	boot
v	view	ʌ	but
θ	throw	ɜː	burn
ð	though	ə	brother
s	sip	eɪ	bay
z	zip	əʊ	bone
ʃ	fresh	aɪ	by
ʒ	measure	aʊ	bound
h	hot	ɔɪ	boy
m	sum	ɪə	beer
n	sun	eə	bare
ŋ	sung	ʊə	poor
l	lot	eɪə	player
r	rot	əʊə	lower
j	yet	aɪə	tire
w	wet	aʊə	flower
		ɔɪə	employer
		i	happy
		u	annual

Special signs

/ˈ/ shows main stress

/ˌ/ shows secondary stress

/ʳ/ at the end of a word means that /r/ is usually pronounced when the next word begins with a vowel sound

Vowels

1 Write the word in normal letters.

a /tɒp/ ....*top*........
b /fɪt/ ....
c /fiːt/ ....
d /hed/ ....
e /hɑːd/ ....
f /mʌd/ ....
g /bæd/ ....
h /bɔːd/ ....
i /wʊd/ ....
j /fuːd/ ....
k /bɜːd/ ....
l /bʌtə/ ....

Consonants

2 Write the word in normal letters.

a /hɑːt/ ....*heart*.......
b /kʌm/ ....
c /ruːd/ ....
d /gest/ ....
e /dʒʌmp/ ....
f /lɪv/ ....
g /freʃ/ ....
h /θɪn/ ....
i /ðiːz/ ....
j /wɒtʃ/ ....
k /bæŋ/ ....
l /plezeə/ ....
m /jɒgɜːt/ ....

Diphthongs

3 Write the word in normal letters.

a /geɪtɪd/ ....*gated*.......
b /maʊs/ ....
c /faɪt/ ....
d /weə/ ....
e /klaʊd/ ....
f /tʃɪə/ ....
g /tɔɪ/ ....
h /steɪt/ ....
i /tʊə/ ....
j /taʊə/ ....
k /faɪə/ ....
l /sləʊə/ ....
m /lɔːjə/ ....

4 Write these words in phonemic script.

a student /stjuːdənt/
b weather /........................../
c English /........................../
d advanced /........................../
e worth /........................../
f joke /........................../
g fork /........................../
h chain /........................../
i repeat /........................../
j happier /........................../
k module /........................../
l houses /........................../

Pearson Education Limited
Edinburgh Gate
Harlow
Essex CM20 2JE
England
and Associated Companies throughout the world.

www.longman.com/cuttingedge

First published 2003
Fourth impression 2005
ISBN 0 582 501741

Set in 9/13pt ITC Stone Informal
and 10/13pt Congress Sans

Printed in Malaysia, KHL

Illustrated by Gerry Ball, Neil Chapman, Celia Hart, Connie Jude, Chris Pavely, Simon Rumble, Jerry Tapscott

Designed by Jennifer Coles

Photo acknowledgements
The publishers are grateful to the following for their permission to reproduce copyright photographs.
Heather Angel / Natural Visions page 74 top; AP Photos page 44 top right; Corbis page 37; James Davies Worldwide page 5; Education Photos page 36; Mary Evans Picture Library page 67; Exile Images page 8 (Howard Davies); Getty / Image Bank page 37; Ronald Grant Archive page 60 top right; Mission page 60 bottom left; NATUREpl.com page 74 bottom (Conrad Maufe); PA Photos page 60 bottom right; Popperfoto page 29 bottom left; Reuters page 6 (Nick Didlick / Popperfoto); Rex pages 44 bottom left, 45; Shout Pictures page 29 top right; Science Photo Library page 74 middle (Michael McCoy) Still Pictures page 46 (Richard Pike); Travel-Ink page 7 (Andrew Harris); Zoological Society of London page 35

Picture Research by Kevin Brown.

The cover photo has been kindly supplied by Getty Images/ Image Bank.

Acknowledgements
The publishers and authors would like to thank the following people and institutions for their feedback and comments during the development of the material:

Wendy Armstrong, The British Council, Milan, and Robert Armitage, International House, Barcelona, for their valuable feedback; Jenny Colley (Senior Publisher); Naomi Tasker (Senior Editor); Tanya Whatling (Freelance Editor); Alma Gray (Freelance Electronic Media Producer); Jennifer Coles (Freelance Designer).

We are grateful to the following for permission to reproduce copyright material:
Aurum Press Limited for extracts from *Nicole Kidman: The Biography* by Lucy Ellis and Bryony Sutherland; Constable & Robinson for jokes and limericks from *The Mammoth Book of Jokes* edited by Geoff Tibballs; Elliott Right Way Books for an extract from *The Polite Approach: A Handbook of Etiquette* by Moira Redmond published by Elliott Right Way Books; HarperCollins Publishers Ltd for an extract from *Family Life* by Sally Magnusson © Sally Magnusson and The Week Ltd for the articles 'Brittney Pringle, a nine-month old baby from Perth' published in *The Week* issue 290 20th January 2001, 'New Yorker Alvin Eykers is divorcing his wife' published in *The Week* issue 292 3rd February 2001, 'An Ohio woman, Addie Crawley got a shock' published in *The Week* issue 299 24th March 2001, 'A British motorist lost her way' published in *The Week* issue 308 26th May 2001, 'An American housewife is offering psychic consultations to troubled pets' published in *The Week* issue 341 19th January 2002, 'The quest for immortality' published in *The Week* issue 360 1st June 2002, 'A tiger's comeback' published in *The Week* issue 361 8th June 2002 and 'Novice climber Leonardo Diaz got stranded' published in *The Week* issue 366 13th July 2002.

In some instances we have been unable to trace the owners of copyright material and we would appreciate any information that would enable us to do so.